LOT

AN

1 DEC

Dedicated to the memory of
Ann McAdam

EDINBURGH GEOLOGICAL SOCIETY

LOTHIAN GEOLOGY

AN EXCURSION GUIDE

Edited by

A. D. McADAM   E. N. K. CLARKSON

SCOTTISH ACADEMIC PRESS

EDINBURGH

Published by
Scottish Academic Press Ltd
33 Montgomery Street, Edinburgh, EH7 5JX

First published in 1960

This edition 1986

SBN 7073 0385 0 Paper Bound
SBN 7073 0384 2 Cloth Bound

British Library Cataloguing in Publications data

McAdam, A.D.
Lothian geology: an excursion guide.
1. Geology——Scotland——Lothian
I. Title   II. Clarkson, E.N.K.
554.13′2   QE264

ISBN 0-7073-0385-0

Printed in Great Britain by

CONTENTS

ILLUSTRATIONS

Maps (continued)

Tables

Figures

Fossil drawings by E. N. K. Clarkson, other drawings by A. D. McAdam

Cover plate by T. Bain, other plates by A. D. McAdam

ix

PREFACE

EDINBURGH GEOLOGY was first published in 1960 and its successor, THE GEOLOGY OF THE LOTHIANS AND SOUTH EAST SCOTLAND, in 1975. This third edition, LOTHIAN GEOLOGY, concentrates on the Lothian Region, and excursions outwith the region have been omitted. Several excursions have been updated or rewritten. New excursions include Building Stones of Edinburgh, Tantallon-St Baldreds, Lammermuir Deans, River North Esk, Paraffin Young Heritage Trail, River Avon and Bathgate Hills. The excursions give opportunities to view the wide range of Palaeozoic sedimentary and igneous rocks in age found within the region, along with landforms and deposits resulting from the Quaternary glaciation. A new introduction describes the rocks, minerals, fossils and structures to be found in the region and the geological processes which produced them.

The excursion guide is aimed at professional and amateur geologists, students, teachers and schoolchildren. While much can be learned by oneself, more insight can be gained by joining geology classes and societies such as the Edinburgh Geological Society. All are encouraged to follow the 'Geological Code of Conduct'.

The editors acknowledge their debt to the authors, to draughtsmen and to photographers. A particular debt is due to the previous editors, Dr D. Grant, the late Dr G. H. Mitchell, Prof. E. K. Walton, Prof. G. Y. Craig and Prof. P. McL. D. Duff. Acknowledgement is also made for help from the Edinburgh Geological Society, the British Geological Survey, the Grant Institute of Geology and the Royal Museum of Scotland.

A. D. McADAM
E. N. K. CLARKSON

INTRODUCTION

EDINBURGH geologists are fortunate in the remarkable variety of rocks and landscape features to be seen in the Lothian Region, within a short distance of the city. From the beginnings of geology in the eighteenth century with the Father of Modern Geology, James Hutton, the area has attracted many geologists and been the scene of several fundamental discoveries in the science. The region offers the geologist opportunities to study stratigraphy, sedimentology, volcanology, structural geology, glaciology, the history of geology and the influence of geology on the environment. Some localities are suitable for collecting fossils, rocks and minerals.

The Lothian Region slopes up from the shores of the Firth of Forth to the watersheds formed by the Moorfoot Hills and Lammermuir Hills, which are made of Lower Palaeozoic rocks, across the Southern Upland Fault. Plains of glacially-covered Devonian and Carboniferous sedimentary rocks are broken by numerous crags and hills of volcanic and intrusive rocks of the same ages. New hills are man-made bings of colliery spoil and spent oil-shale, while quarries and pits have been cut to obtain limestone, dolerite, sandstone, clay, sand and gravel.

Drainage into the Forth follows the main Lower Palaeozoic structural grain parallel to the Southern Upland Fault. The main rivers, the Avon, Almond, Water of Leith, North Esk, South Esk and Tyne all flow from south-west to north-east. Tributary drainage flows north from the Moorfoot, Lammermuir and Pentland Hills. Population in the region centres around Edinburgh, and to a lesser extent at Livingston and in the Esk Valley. Intense cultivation has taken place on the low ground particularly in the granary of East Lothian, grading up to cattle and sheep pasture in the uplands. The higher rocky hills form peat- and heather-covered moorlands.

For the geologist the best exposures are along the coast, in some of the incised river valleys and in the volcanic uplands.

1

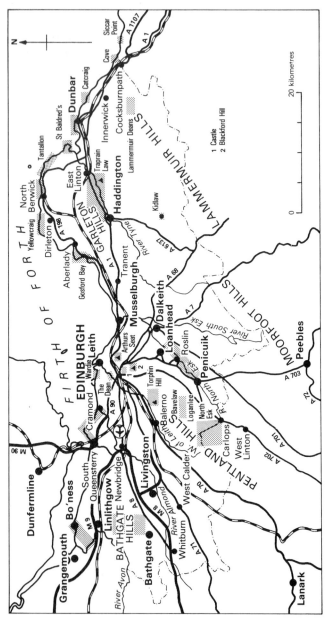

MAP 1. Lothian Region and the location of the excursions

Access to the region is by bus, train or air (Map 1). Within the region a network of roads makes for good accessibility by car or private coach. Lothian Region Transport run service buses within the City of Edinburgh, and green and cream Eastern Scottish and Lowland Scottish service buses, based in St Andrew Square, serve the country areas (Map 5).

Rocks

Rocks are all formed of crystalline or amorphous minerals. Some rocks consist of only one sort of mineral but the great majority of rocks are composed of several kinds of mineral. There are three main groups of rocks, known as igneous, sedimentary and metamorphic. Only rocks of the first two groups occur in the Lothian Region.

Igneous rocks solidified from an originally molten material called magma. As the magma cooled crystals of different minerals grew, becoming interlocked. The composition of the magma and the rate of cooling determine the kind and size of minerals formed. Igneous rocks are classified by the type and proportion of these minerals, and whether the grain size is coarse, medium or fine. When molten magma reaches the surface it produces extrusive rocks in the form of lavas which cool quickly and hence are generally fine-grained. On the other hand, rising magma can solidify deep below the surface to form plutonic rocks which, as they cool slowly, tend to be medium- or coarse-grained.

Sedimentary rocks are mostly the result of weathering of many different kinds of rock, transport of pebbles, sand and mud by river, sea and wind action, and deposition of the detritus as layer after layer of sediment in sea, river, lake or on land. Sediments, accumulated and buried over enormous periods, harden as water is squeezed out and the individual grains are compacted and cemented together. Thus sands becomes *sandstones*, muds become *shales* and gravels become *conglomerates*. Other sedimentary rocks result from chemical precipitation out of solution, notably *limestone*, while yet other rocks incorporate remains of animal or plant life, e.g. shells may form a *shelly limestone* and plants may form *coal*. Detrital material in sedimentary rocks derives from pre-existing rocks, whether igneous, metamorphic or sedimentary. Sedimentary detritus may have been incorporated in earlier sediments and recycled several times.

One group of rocks not easily classified are *pyroclastic rocks*, derived from volcanic ash which falls through the atmosphere and is often deposited in water to form layered rocks. Although formed by sedimentary processes, the material is igneous in origin and these rocks are normally grouped with the igneous rocks.

Metamorphic rocks were originally sedimentary or igneous rocks which have been altered to new textures and minerals by the action of heat, pressure and friction, often during more than one episode. Thus shales have been altered to *slates* or *schists*, sandstones to *quartzites* or *psammites*, limestones to *marbles* and basic igneous rocks to *amphibolites* or *epidiorites*. Metamorphic rocks are virtually absent from the Lothian Region. However, low-grade metamorphic rocks form much of the adjacent Southern Uplands south of the Southern Upland Fault and high-grade metamorphic rocks form most of the Highlands north of the Highland Boundary Fault. Fragments of metamorphic rocks derived from both areas do occur locally, as boulders in Palaeozoic conglomerates and as glacially transported boulders called erratics.

Sedimentary Rocks

Sedimentary rocks are commonly layered. Most, though not all, formed under water or in air by accumulation of detrital particles—*clastic rocks*. Others have formed by precipitation from solution through chemical or organic agency—*organo-chemical deposits*. These unconsolidated deposits have then been compacted, often cemented and may also have undergone chemical change (diagenesis) after deposition.

There are many different kinds of sedimentary rocks. They can be classified in various ways depending upon how the classification is to be used. Both clastic and organo-chemical rocks are common in the Lothian Region.

Clastic rocks, also known as *fragmental* or *detrital* deposits, are formed of fragments of earlier rocks. During the weathering and transportation processes which produce a new sedimentary rock the more resistant minerals of the original rock survive while other minerals break up and dissolve. A granite, which consists of quartz, feldspar and mica, will for example normally only contribute the highly resistant quartz to a clastic sediment. Mica and feldspar, being far less resistant, only occur in a clastic rock in which the material is of local derivation and has not travelled far.

Clastic rocks can be classified in the field in three separate categories, according to grain size:

RUDACEOUS rocks (grain size > 1 cm) consist of pebbles, cobbles or boulders set in a finer matrix. In *conglomerates* the pebbles are rounded during transport, and the material of which they are composed is derived from older rocks often some distance away. *Breccias* have angular pebbles and are of more local derivation as the pebbles have not travelled far enough to have become rounded. These should not be confused with *fault-breccias*, formed in fault zones, where the rock has been smashed by fault movement.

ARENACEOUS rocks (grain size 0·1 mm–1 cm) include many kinds of generally sandy rock in which the rock has been sorted to dominantly one grain-size. *Grits* are coarse sandstone, or sandstones with angular grains. In *sandstones* the bulk of the rock consists of quartz particles, cemented by calcareous, siliceous, or ferruginous material or with a muddy matrix. *Arkose* is a less mature sandstone containing an appreciable amount of feldspar. *Greywacke* is an ill-sorted rock with much quartz, but with minerals and pebbles of different compositions in a very muddy matrix.

ARGILLACEOUS rocks (grain size < 0·1 mm). Rocks of finer material with grain size 0·01–0·1 mm are known as *siltstones*. *Mudstones* with grain size less than 0·01 mm may have some fine quartz grains but are mainly formed of clay minerals and may also be calcareous or iron-rich. *Shales* are mudstones or siltstones which are fissile, splitting along bedding planes because they contain flat-lying clay minerals. Some *limestones* of detrital origin may be grouped here as they consist mainly of fragments of earlier limestones, or of shells and shell fragments.

Organo-chemical sediments are rocks that have precipitated from solution, often wholly or partly due to bacterial or other organic activity. *Limestones* consist of calcium carbonate ($CaCO_3$). Many limestones have formed entirely as chemical precipitates. *Oolitic limestones* for example consist of closely packed carbonate spheres, which grew where water saturated with calcium carbonate washed backwards and forwards over a shallow sea floor, often in warm, highly saline lagoons. Some limestones are converted to *dolomite* ($CaCO_3.MgCO_3$) which has a characteristic yellow colour. The chemical changes occurred in warm shallow water in the presence of CO_2, either contemporaneous with or later than deposition. *Organic limestones*, also known as *bioclastic limestones*, are formed from coral reefs or at least partly of shells and shell fragments. Other such limestones are laminated rocks, the result of lime precipitation by algal mats known as *stromatolites*, which trap and bind clastic material into many forms.

Ironstones and iron-rich rocks formed in various conditions. Hematite (Fe_2O_3) was precipitated under oxidising conditions, siderite ($FeCO_3$) formed in a moderately reducing environment, whilst the presence of pyrite (FeS_2) is indicative of highly reducing conditions of formation. Some ironstones are secondary in origin forming long after deposition.

The most important carbonaceous deposits are *coal* and *oil-shale*. Coal formed in fresh-water environments from peat, the altered remains of plants, the shapes of which can sometimes still be seen, though plant specimens are better preserved in the associated siltstones and mudstones. Many varieties of coal can be distinguished. *Bituminous* coals have alternate bright, clarain, and dull, fusain, layers in which different types of plant remains occur, and have prominent joints, cleats. *Cannel* coal is unlaminated and dull, consisting mainly of plant spores, the remains of oil-bearing algae, and fine detrital material. *Oil-shales* are fine-grained rocks similar to cannel coal, in which the organic matter of algal origin is mixed with a higher proportion of detrital material, and from which oil can be extracted by heating. The oil-shales were deposited in a large lake.

Sedimentology, the detailed study of sedimentary rocks in the field and in the laboratory, can reveal a great deal about the environments in which the rocks were deposited. Thus different kinds of conglomerates and sandstones could have been deposited on a beach, as an alluvial fan, as a flash-flood deposit or in a braided river meandering through a flood plain. Siltstones and mudstones on the other hand form in quieter conditions. The fine fraction of which they are composed took longer to settle out of suspension and often was carried far from land. Limestones usually accumulate in warm shallow waters where there is little input of terrigenous material. Seatclays are grey carbonaceous clays found below coals and are a kind of fossil soil.

All inferences about the nature of the depositional environment must of course be related to the regional context. Any fossils in the rocks may also give useful indications as to the nature of the original environment.

Sedimentary Structures. As well as composition and grain size, other indicators about the nature of the depositional environment are the sedimentary structures often found within the rock. These structures can be formed during deposition, produced after deposition, or are the result of contemporaneous activity of organisms in the sediment—trace fossils.

Structures formed in water-laid clastic sediments deposited in alluvial channels, include *laminar beds*, *ripple-marks*, and *cross-bedding*. When the current bringing in the sediment was very weak, the upper surface of the sediment remained unmarked and the layers have a flat surface. As the current increased, however, ripple-marks formed. In very fine sediments these would form at a low current velocity; coarser sands would require a higher current strength. Tidally influenced ripples are *symmetrical* due to the waves washing to and fro, but ripples in a unidirectional current are *asymmetrical*, the steeper slope facing upstream. With increasing current strength, much larger *megaripples* form, and eventually subaqueous dunes and *sandwaves*. When current strength is extreme and the sediment coarse, dune-like structures known as *antidunes* move upstream against the current, as sand is continually streamed off the surface of one dune to be built up on the facing slope of the next. Finer sediment at this velocity forms planar beds for the current moves so rapidly that no structures can form. When a great deal of sediment comes down at moderate current velocities, *climbing ripples* of sloping piled-up sets, a few centimetres thick will form; they can be seen in section migrating obliquely upwards through the sediment.

A very common type of structure in sedimentary rocks is *cross-bedding*, in which the laminar beds, *foresets*, form slightly curving sigmoidal surfaces lying obliquely to the horizontal. These are likewise due to the movement of sand particles in migrating subaqueous dunes or sandwaves. Windblown sand can form dunes in which the sets are even larger, several metres thick. The water-lain sets may be tabular, with more or less planar surfaces bounding the units. On the other hand, the lower surface may, in cross-section be curving and erosional in cases where a migrating channel has cut into earlier formed channels, before deposition took place. This is known as *trough* cross-stratification. Cross-bedding directions are very useful indicators of current and transportation directions. *Herringbone* cross-bedding, where successive sets go in different directions, is typical of shallow tidal water.

Very significant sedimentary structures occur in greywackes (such as form much of the Southern Uplands and the North Esk Inlier). Greywacke beds carry a characteristic sequence of internal structures indicating deposition by occasional turbidity currents, rapidly flowing down a slope and carrying suspended clouds of debris. The flow is initially erosional, then depositional. In the erosional phase of such a flow scurrying vortices cut characteristic bulbous, triangular *flute-marks* into the cohesive mud surface over which it flows. These immediately fill with coarse sand, which becomes finer towards the top of the unit so that the lower part of the unit is thus graded in terms of grain size. Towards the top of the unit the waning current has still been strong enough to form ripple-marks. Thereafter only the finest particles settle out of suspension as mud before the next turbidity current. Deposition was episodic, with long periods of quiescence alternating with rapid periods of deposition. Linear scrapes, known as *tool-marks* occur where a pebble or a shell within the flow has cut a groove in the mud. These *sole-markings* (all markings on the lower surface of a turbidite unit) are normally only seen on the lower surface of the sandstone unit when the underlying mud, now compacted to shale, has been washed away. Sole-markings may be modified after deposition by loading, when the heavy sand sinks down into the soft mud below, squeezing out the water and forming bulbous irregular masses called *load-markings*. Alternatively sediment may become *contorted* through slumping.

The churning activities of animals, dwelling on or in the sediment, and foraging on its surface or mining within it may also greatly affect the sediment after deposition, often destroying primary laminations entirely. This is known as *bioturbation*. Some particularly clear *trace-fossils*, on the other hand, seen in clastic and other sediments, are given biological names, even if their maker is unknown. Trace-fossils are often good environmental indicators. In general terms makers of vertical tubes and U-shaped burrows feeding on suspended particles are common in littoral and shallow water sediments, whilst animals which feed upon sediments, either by mining or by surface grazing, are commoner in deeper waters. Fossil soils, called *seatclays* or *seatrocks*, have been bioturbated and the sedimentary structures destroyed by roots and rootlets commonly preserved within them.

Igneous Rocks

Igneous rocks are formed from molten rock (magma) which originates in chambers at depths of several kilometres under the earth's surface. They can be divided into extrusive rocks, formed where the magma reached the surface and erupted from volcanoes, and intrusive rocks formed by magma which failed to reach the surface and as a result solidified underground.

Volcanic eruptions from central or fissure vents produce *lava flows* during the less violent episodes, while volcanic ash and bombs, lithified into *tuff* and *agglomerate*, result from more explosive events. Most eruptions in the Lothian Region were subaerial. There are no records of pillow lavas derived from submarine volcanoes, though many tuffs between the lava flows are bedded and water-lain.

The form taken by intrusive rocks depends on the type of magma, the force of intrusion and the country rock (Figure 1). A *sill* is a sheet-like intrusion, commonly flat-lying, forced between layers of strata, as at Salisbury Crags. Vertical sheets, filling cracks discordant to the bedding, and called *dykes*, as can be seen on North Berwick shore. A *laccolith* forms where more viscous acid magma domes up the overlying strata to a mushroom shape; Traprain Law is an excellent example. A *plug* is a cylindrical intrusion filling a volcanic vent, as at Castle Rock, North Berwick Law and the

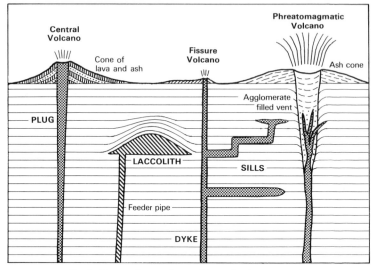

Fig 1. Forms of extrusive and intrusive igneous rocks

Bass Rock. Other volcanic vents are filled with agglomerate, a mixture of blocks of country rock, volcanic bombs and ash, intruded with irregular minor dykes and sills. The nature of the infill varies with depth within the volcano (Leys 1982).

Only a small number of the many igneous rock types described worldwide are found within the Lothian Region. The common fine-grained rocks found as lavas vary from basic to acid, within the series basalt-andesite-trachyte-rhyolite. This series show a decrease in ferromagnesian minerals (mainly clinopyroxene) and an increase in feldspathic minerals (mainly plagioclase). Examples of all these rocks occur in the Lower Devonian lavas of the Pentland Hills. The Lower Carboniferous alkaline suite, however, is made up dominantly of olivine-basalts, with subordinate trachybasalts. These olivine-basalts are porphyritic and the scheme of MacGregor (1928), subdividing the basalts using the type and size of the phenocrysts, has been widely used on Geological Survey maps. Comparison with the chemical classification of Macdonald (1975) is given in Table 1. Trachybasalts from this suite are mostly mugearites in which the feldspar is dominantly oligoclase.

	MacGregor (1928)	Phenocrysts		Macdonald (1975)
		abundant	may occur	
Macroporphyritic (>2 mm)	**Markle**	plagioclase	olivine iron oxides	macroporphyritic: olivine-plagioclase ± iron oxides-phyric basalt, basaltic hawaiite or hawaiite
	Dunsapie	plagioclase clinopyroxene olivine	iron oxides	macroporphyritic: olivine-plagioclase-clinopyroxene-iron oxides-phyric basaltic hawaiite or olivine-clino-pyroxene-plagioclase-phyric basalt
	Craiglockhart	clinopyroxene olivine		ankaramite
Microporphyric (<2 mm)	**Jedburgh**	plagioclase olivine	iron oxides	microphyric: olivine-plagioclase ±iron oxides-phyric hawaiite, basaltic hawaiite or occasionally basalt
	Dalmeny	olivine	plagioclase clino-pyroxene	microphyric: olivine-basalt or olivine-plagioclase-clinopyroxene-phyric basalt
	Hillhouse	olivine	clino-pyroxene	microphyric: olivine-basalt or olivine-clinopyroxene-phyric basalt

Iron oxide commonly occurs as iron-titanium oxides

TABLE 1. Olivine-basalt nomenclature

Medium- and coarse-grained igneous rocks occur as intrusions. Most are related to the Devonian and Carboniferous volcanism. The great majority are of dolerite, the medium-grained equivalent of basalt. These may be undersaturated, with felspathoid minerals, as in the Namurian teschenite suite, or oversaturated as in the Stephanian quartz-dolerite and tholeiite suite. More extremely differentiated rocks are the mafic basanite-monchiquite suite and felspathoid-bearing phonolite, both associated with the Garleton Hills Volcanic Rocks.

Fossils

Fossils are the preserved remains of animals and plants which are commonly found in different kinds of sedimentary rock. They include not only 'body fossils' but also trace-fossils discussed above (p. 9). The majority of fossils preserved in rocks are the remains of marine invertebrates. Less commonly, more unusual fossil assemblages which contain brackish or freshwater fossil fish and amphibians, have accumulated in deposits in lagoons or estuaries.

The importance of fossils in geology is twofold. Firstly, they provide an unrivalled means of stratigraphic correlation.

Although the Earth's history is very long, some 4600 million years, only rocks deposited in the last 570 million contain abundant remains of fossil animals, represented by their hard shells buried soon after death. From that time, marking the start of the Cambrian system, the faunas change continually reflecting the origins, zenith and extinction of particular kinds of organisms, and of the communities they lived in. Each level of the rock record thus possesses a unique assemblage of fossils, characteristic of that time period during which the rocks were deposited and of no other. The succession of such faunas is the basis of *biostratigraphy*—the division of the rock record into ordered stratigraphic units, recognisable by their fossil remains. Fossils give a relative chronology; one can immediately recognise a fossil assemblage containing trilobites, for example, as belonging to the Palaeozoic, for thereafter trilobites died out, and later rocks never contain their remains. When faunas replace each other in rapid succession, particular time-units or zones can be defined accurately, and such zones may span less than a million years. Fossils of course, cannot give more than a relative time scale, absolute dates in terms of millions of years have to be supplied by other techniques such as radiometric dating.

Fossils have been used in stratigraphy for more than 150 years, but increasingly they have also been found of great

Fig 2. Silurian (Upper Llandovery) fossils from the North Esk Inlier

1. *Acernaspis sufferta* (Lamont) × 1
2. *Encrinurus expansus* Haswell × 1
3. *Craspedobolbina (Mitrobeyrichia) impendens* (Haswell),
   (*a*) female, (*b*) tecnomorph (male) × 5
4. *Cyrtia exporrecta* Wahlenberg, internal mould × 1
5. *Skenidioides lewisii* (Davidson), shell preserved × 2
6. *Leptaena* sp., internal mould, pedicle valve × 1
7. *Eoplectodonta penkillensis* (Reed), (*a*) dorsal view,
   (*b*) brachial valve, internal mould, (*c*) pedicle valve,
   external mould × 1·5
8. *Atrypa reticularis* (Linnaeus) shell preserved × 1
9. *Visbyella* sp., (*a*) shell preserved, (*b*) internal mould of
   brachial valve × 1·5
10. *Dicoeolosia verneuiliana* (Beecher), shell preserved × 1·5
11. *Coolinia applanata* (Salter), shell preserved × 1
12. *Dalejina polygramma pentlandica* (Davidson), internal
    mould × 1

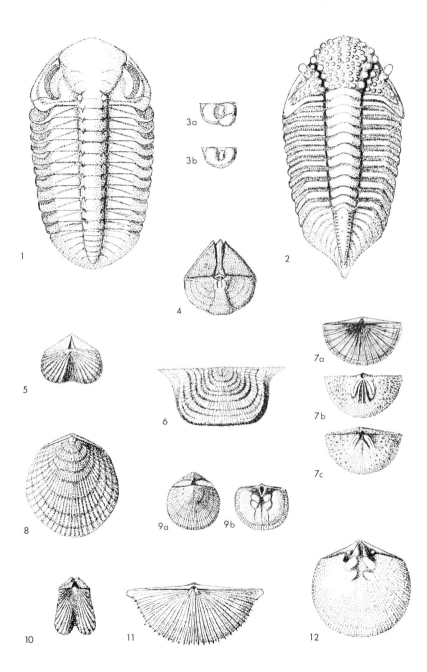

value in interpreting ancient sedimentary environments. Thus faunas which lived in shallow open seas for example have a very different aspect to those which inhabited quiet brackish water lagoons. Moreover fossil assemblages with bivalve shells still held together were probably deposited in quiet water, whilst storm-generated shell banks can be distinguished by the randomly orientated and often fragmentary shells.

The rocks in the Lothian Region consist entirely of Palaeozoic rocks which in places have a cover of Quaternary sediments. The Silurian is marine, lagoonal and freshwater to desert, the Devonian is entirely fluviatile and desert, while the Carboniferous has alternating marine, lacustrine, estuarine and lagoonal environments.

In early marine sediments the commonest fossils (Figures 2, 3) are the *brachiopods*, a kind of two-valved shellfish which fed upon suspended particles. The brachiopods lost their dominance at the end of the Palaeozoic, though there are some living forms. The *bivalves*, superficially similar in being two-valved, though quite unrelated since they are molluscs, took over as the main sea-floor dwelling filter-feeders. In both the Silurian and the Carboniferous of the region are found environments favouring *corals*, which like their living counterparts can be solitary or compound. In the Carboniferous some corals formed flat-lying banks though not truly reefs. Various kinds of *echinoderms*, (the calcite-

FIG 3. CARBONIFEROUS MARINE FOSSILS

1. *Lithostrotion junceum* (Fleming), (*a*) transverse section of corollaites, (*b*) part of colony × 1; Viséan
2. *Aulophyllum fungites* (Fleming), (*a*) transverse section, (*b*) single individual with rejuvenescent buds × 0·75; Viséan
3. *Dictyoclostus semireticulatus* (Martin), (*a*) ventral view, (*b*) lateral view × 0·75; Viséan
4. *Eomarginifera setosa* (Phillips), (*a*) ventral view, (*b*) dorsal view × 1; Viséan
5. *Composita ambigua* (J. Sowerby), (*a*) dorsal view with part of the shell broken away exposing the spiralium, (*b*) lateral view × 1; Viséan
6. *Pugnoides pleurodon* (Phillips), (*a*) dorsal view, (*b*) anterior view × 0·75; Viséan
7. *Spirifer striatus* (Martin) × 1; Viséan
8. *Dunbarella papyracea* (J. de C. Sowerby) × 1; Westphalian.

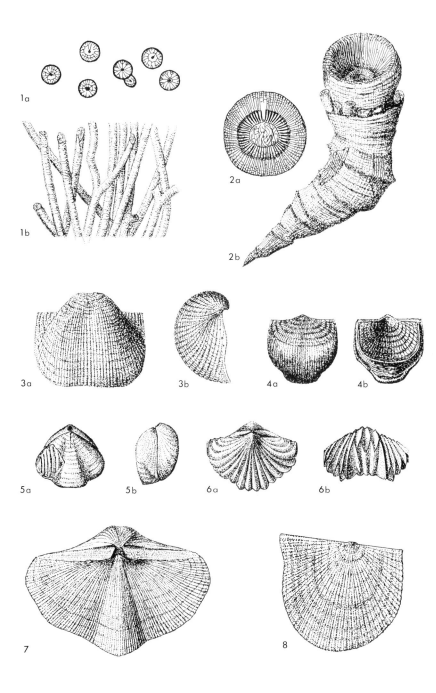

plated group that includes sea urchins and starfish), are found in both Silurian and Carboniferous, especially commonly in the latter. *Crinoids*, or sea lilies, are echinoderms, superficially like flowers, which attached to the sea floor by a long stalk, and used their radiating arms to trap suspended sediment. Many limestones are largely composed of the plates and stems of these fragile animals. *Bryozoans*, also preserved in limestones, are delicate calcite colonies with hundreds of tiny cavities in each of which lived small polyp-like animal, also a suspension feeder. Common in the Silurian but rare in the Carboniferous are *trilobites*, an entirely extinct group of mobile sea floor dwelling arthropods which had a trilobed outer body and often large compound eyes. These moved over the sea floor upon rather feeble legs, and may have fed as scavengers or mud-ingesters. Deeper water sediments, especially black shales of Silurian age, contain the remains of *graptolites*, another extinct group, which were delicate floating colonies of small polyp-like animals, feeding on suspended material and micro-organisms in the plankton. These lived in the open sea and because they drifted widely across seas and into quiet shallow water, they are of great stratigraphical value.

Many fossils found in the region are often very well preserved. In limestones, the shells can retain their original form and are often relatively unaltered chemically. The outer surfaces of the shells are clearly seen when the rock is

Fig 4. Carboniferous lagoonal and non-marine fossils

1. *Elonichthys robisoni* Traquair, (*a*) restoration after Traquair
   × 1; (*b*) caudal scale × 8; Viséan
2. *Lingula squamiformis* Phillips × 1; Viséan-Namurian
3. *Orbiculoidea nitida* Phillips, (*a*) brachial valve,
   (*b*) pedicle valve × 2; Viséan-Namurian
4. *Tealliocaris woodwardi* Peach × 4; Viséan
5. *Waterstonella grantonensis* Schram × 10; Viséan
6. *Naiadites modiolaris* J de C Sowerby × 1; Westphalian
7. *Anthracosia planitumida* Trueman × 1·5; Westphalian
8. *Rhizodus hibberti* Traquair, tooth × 0·33; Viséan
9. *Beyrichiopsis plicata* Jones and Kirkby × 16; Viséan-Namurian
10. *Cavellina spola* Robinson × 15; Viséan

Lingula and *Orbiculoidea* are marine fossils tolerant of low salinity.

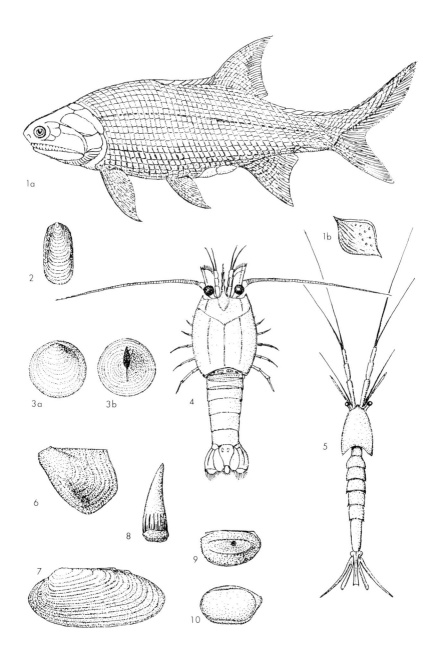

1a

1b

2

3a 3b

4

5

6

8

7

9

10

cracked open. In calcareous mudstones the shells are
commonly crushed. On the other hand (as in the Silurian of
the North Esk Inlier), the shells may be dissolved but leave
their imprint on the matrix. These moulds may show delicate
details of both external and internal structures, for example
the scars of the muscles which brachiopods used to open and
close their shells.

Some Carboniferous rocks in the Lothian Region which
were deposited in a large freshwater or brackish lake and
contain some unusual fossils (Figure 4). These sediments
have the remains of *fishes*, *crustaceans* of shrimp-like form,
freshwater molluscs, and the small bivalved crustaceans
known as *ostracods*; an assemblage of animals quite different
from those living in the seas.

Plants first developed widely and their remains became
abundant in the Carboniferous. Remains of fronds, stems
and even large trunks of these plants, mainly forest trees of
fern and horsetail type, such as *Calamites*, are found in
mudstones, siltstones and sandstones. Roots and rootlets of
the trees, *Stigmaria*, are widely preserved in seatclays and
seatrocks below coal seams.

Structural Geology (Figure 5)

Sedimentary and extrusive igneous rocks are normally laid
down in horizontal layers, called strata. Only in stable shield
areas of the earth's crust do these remain undisturbed.
Elsewhere the rocks are affected sooner or later by movement of the plates that form the earth's crust. The strata then
become variously squeezed and stretched, raised and
lowered, buckled and cracked, heated and intruded with
molten rock, eroded off and buried beneath further layers.

Strata which have buckled are said to be folded. *Folds* can
take many forms, such as *symmetrical* or *asymmetrical*, *overturned*, *recumbent* or *isoclinal*. An arched fold is called an
anticline; a trough fold is a *syncline*. As a result of folding the
strata may remain horizontal or be shallowly, steeply or vertically inclined. The amount and direction of the maximum
slope of a bedding plane is called the *dip*. The *strike* of the
bed is the horizontal line at right angles to the direction of
dip. The *axis* is the direction of a fold while the *axial plane*
depends on the orientation of the *fold limbs*. Axes and axial

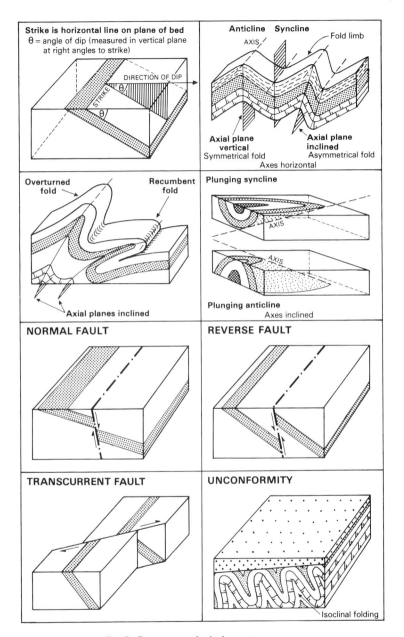

FIG 5. Common geological structures

planes can vary from horizontal to inclined or vertical. Where the axis of a fold is inclined the anticline or syncline is said to be *plunging*. All the rocks in the Lothian Region show the effects of folding in the constantly varying dips. Folds are only rarely exposed, though shallow folds can be seen on the shore, as at Yellowcraig and Catcraig.

Instead of yielding to stress by folding, rocks may fracture and form *faults*. A *normal fault* is produced by tension, a *reverse* or *thrust fault* by pressure and a *transcurrent* or *tear fault* results from relative lateral movement. The *throw* of a fault, the amount of movement, can vary from a centimetre or two to a kilometre or more, as in the Southern Upland Fault. Most of the faulting that has affected rocks in the Lothian Region is normal faulting with fault-planes dipping at 60° to 70°. A notable exception is the Pentland Fault, a major reverse fault. Faults are rarely exposed, partly because fracturing of the rocks make them particularly vulnerable to erosion. Faulting, however, can be inferred from the juxtaposition of rocks of different ages and by the presence of steeply-dipping strata.

Breaks in deposition and the effects of folding can be seen in a structure called an *unconformity*. Older rocks, having been tilted or folded, uplifted and subjected to erosion, have later horizontal layers of sediment deposited on top, at an angle to the older layers. This *angle of unconformity* remains, even if the rocks are subject to further tilting or folding. Arguably the most famous unconformity in the world, where Hutton demonstrated the concept in 1788, is that at Siccar Point. Major unconformities represent periods of mountain-building and folding, and may be used to mark boundaries between different geological systems or groups of strata.

Geological History

The rocks underlying the Lothian Region are typical of those found in the geological heartland of Scotland, the Midland Valley. These rocks belong to only three geological periods, the Silurian, the Devonian (or Old Red Sandstone) and the Carboniferous, covering an age span from over 400 million years ago to about 280 million years ago. The geographical distribution of the rocks is shown on Map 2. The

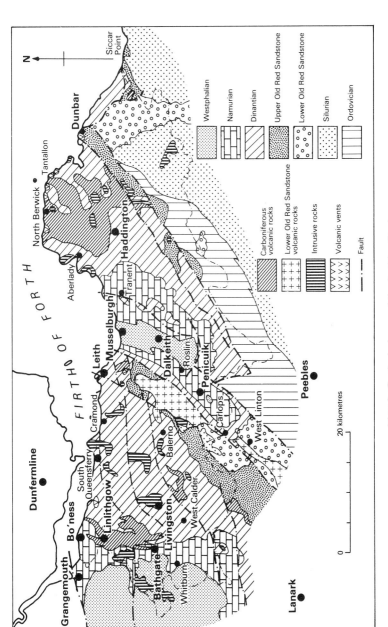

MAP 2. Geological map of the Lothian Region

geological divisions, their age, their typical lithologies and the environments in which they formed are described in Table 2.

In *Silurian* times the area was close to the edge of the Iapetus Ocean, filling with sediment as the ocean closed. Shallow tropical seas abounded with brachiopods, trilobites, molluscs, sea-lilies, starfish and ostracods on the sand, silt or mud sea-bed, while rare planktonic graptolites lived in the waters above. Early jawless fish inhabited coastal lagoons and inland lakes. A transition occurs from grey marine strata of fossiliferous sandstones, siltstones and mudstones, to red terrestrial sandstones later in the Silurian as arid land emerged from the seas. As the sediments changed with changing conditions, so did their contained fauna which was precisely adapted to their environment. Massive mountain-building of the *Caledonian Orogeny* left the once-horizontal Silurian strata tilted vertically (North Esk Inlier and the Pentland Hills Excursions). By late Silurian times the Highland Boundary Fault and the Southern Upland Fault had become active, and the Midland Valley came into existence as a down-faulted block between mountainous terrain to north and south.

During the following *Devonian* Period these high barren mountains left by the orogeny were eroded by water, wind and heat down to level plains. The resulting red continental sandstones gave the period its local name of Old Red Sandstone. In *Lower Old Red Sandstone* times giant alluvial fans ranged along the two boundary faults poured conglomerate (Lammermuir Deans Excursion) into the Midland Valley from the eroding northern and southern mountains. At the same time eruption of basaltic, andesitic and acid lavas and tuffs formed the Pentland Hills Volcanic Rocks (The Pentland Hills and Blackford Hill Excursions). In the Middle Old Red Sandstone further earth-movements uplifted the Pentland Hills and initiated the Pentland and Colinton faults. Large rivers in the less arid *Upper Old Red Sandstone* times gave rise to red fluviatile sandstones with interbedded lacustrine siltstones and mudstones containing rare fish remains. Also present are cornstones, dolomitic limestones that represent leached soil horizons. Red sandstones of this age occur round the north flanks of the

PERIOD	EPOCH/SERIES	AGE	ENVIRONMENT	TYPE OF ROCK/DEPOSIT
QUATERNARY	Post-Glacial	Present day	Temperate land, High sea level	River alluvium, Low raised beach
	Late-Glacial	10000	Sub-arctic, Very high sea level, Arctic	Peat, High raised beach, Sands and gravels
	Glacial	15000	Ice-cap with interglacials	Boulder clay (till)
TERTIARY, CRETACEOUS, JURASSIC, TRIASSIC, PERMIAN	(Gap in geological record)	1 million	Land, temperate to desert, Earthquakes, Mountain building	
CARBONIFEROUS wet	Coal Measures, Passage Group	280 million	Coal swamps, seas, deltas, Rivers, deltas	Igneous intrusions, Coal-bearing sediments, Sandstones, fireclays, Mixed strata
Namurian	Upper Limestone Group, Limestone Coal Group, Lower Limestone Group		Coal swamps, deltas, coral seas	Coal-bearing sediments, Limestone-bearing sediments
Dinantian	Upper Oil-Shale Group, Lower Oil-Shale Group		Freshwater lagoons, deltas	Oil-shale-bearing sediments, Oil-shales, sandstones
	Arthur's Seat Volcanic Rocks, Cementstone Group	345 million	Volcanic eruptions, Coastal, shallow lagoons	Lavas, tuffs, vents, Mixed strata
DEVONIAN (OLD RED SANDSTONE)	Upper Old Red Sandstone, Pentland Hills Volcanic Rocks, Lower Old Red Sandstone	395 million	Rivers, arid desert, Volcanic eruptions, earthquakes, Desert, floods, rivers, Earthquakes, mountain building	Red sandstones, Lavas, tuffs, intrusions, Red conglomerates
SILURIAN	Wenlock, Llandovery	435 million, 500 million	Barren land, Shallow tropical seas	Red sandstones, Fossil-bearing mudstones
ORDOVICIAN				
CAMBRIAN		570 million		

TABLE 2. Geological timetable

Pentland Hills, Moorfoot Hills and Lammermuir Hills and are exposed on the coast in the east (Siccar Point and Dunbar Excursions).

By the start of the *Carboniferous* Period the region had been worn down to low-lying, afforested coastal plains. Land and sea fought a constant battle for supremacy over the plains through the Carboniferous, producing repeated rhythmic cycles of marine, deltaic, freshwater and fluviatile sedimentation. At the start of each cycle dense lycopod forest swamps, resembling in many ways the mangrove swamps of today, gave rise to peat and coal. Subsidence of the land led to inundation by seas in which marine shells thrived in the muddy seabed and coral reefs flourished in clear tropical waters. Rivers built deltas of mud, silt and sand, reclaiming the land from the sea. In freshwater lagoons along the new coast and on the alluvial plains precipitation of lime produced freshwater limestones and thin cementstone beds, or flourishing micro-organisms gave rise to bituminous mudstones and oil-shales. Forests became re-established on the reclaimed land, the tree roots forming thick leached soils that are now represented by the seatearths or seatclays under each coal. At different times during the Carboniferous, conditions favoured thick development of particular parts of the cycles while other parts were thin or absent. Thus individual groups of strata have thick development of economic minerals such as coal, limestone, oil-shale, sandstone or fireclay, and the outcrop distribution of these minerals has influenced industrial and population growth within the region.

In the Midland Valley the Carboniferous strata are divided into groups, mainly on the basis of marine bands. In terms of age, the groups can be classified (Table 2) into the Dinantian (equivalent to the Carboniferous Limestone Series of England), the Namurian (equivalent to the Millstone Grit Series) and the Westphalian (equivalent to the Coal Measures).

The earliest *Dinantian* strata, belonging to the *Cementstone Group*, are thinly-bedded freshwater mudstones, siltstones and sandstones with thin lagoonal dolomitic limestones (cementstones) and poor non-marine faunas. These strata underlie much of the City of Edinburgh.

Volcanic activity returned throughout the region as the well-preserved Arthur's Seat Volcano poured out basaltic lavas and tuffs (Arthur's Seat and The Castle Hill Excursions), and other volcanoes erupted at Craiglockhart Hill and Corston Hill in the west. The contemporaneous Garleton Hills Volcanic Rocks, containing basaltic lavas and tuffs overlain by trachytic lavas and tuffs, extend from the north coast of East Lothian (North Berwick Excursion) to the Garleton Hills (Garleton Hills Excursion). Thick fluviatile or deltaic sandstones, such as the Craigleith Sandstone, Ravelston Sandstone and Hailes Sandstone and thick mudstones such as the Wardie Shales, are features of the *Lower Oil-Shale Group* which underlies northern Edinburgh and part of West Lothian (Wardie and Granton Shore and The Dean Excursions). Large quarries, like Hailes Quarry, are now mostly infilled and built over, concealing the industry which not only supplied high quality building stone for the New Town and suburbs of Edinburgh, but also exported to London and continental Europe. Also vanished is the West Lothian oil-shale industry which mined and distilled the oil-shale to produce oil and chemical by-products for over a century up to 1962. The main oil-shale seams worked were the Pumpherston Shale in the Lower Oil-Shale Group and the Camps, Dunnet, Broxburn and Fells seams in the *Upper Oil-Shale Group* (South Queensferry-Cramond Excursion). In East Lothian these lowest three groups of the Carboniferous have not been separately recognised, the strata being known as the *Calciferous Sandstone Measures* (North Berwick, Dunbar and Pease Bay to Cove Excursions). The earliest marine incursions which took place during deposition of the Lower Oil-Shale Group gave rise to marine bands, known variously as the Pumpherston Shell Bed, Macgregor Marine Bands or Cove Marine Bands. Long-lasting marine conditions were established later in *Lower Limestone Group* times. Clear tropical seas gave rise to thick fossiliferous marine limestones which can be correlated from East Lothian through Midlothian to West Lothian (Gosford Bay-Aberlady Point, Catcraig and Bathgate Hills Excursions). These limestones, formerly worked extensively, are now worked opencast at Oxwellmains, near Dunbar, and mined and quarried at Middleton, south of Edinburgh.

At the start of *Namurian* times debris from tropical forests produced the many thick coal seams of the *Limestone Coal Group*. Two prominent marine incursions in the otherwise deltaic sediments, the Johnstone Shell Bed and the Black Metals Marine Band, enable correlation of the coal seams. There are presently only two modern deep mines in the Midlothian Coalfield, one old mine in West Lothian and one large opencast site in the East Lothian Coalfield still remaining from the large number of collieries that once existed in the region. In the *Upper Limestone Group* the coal seams are thin as are the marine limestones which provide distinctive marker horizons. The Index Limestone marks the base, followed in upward sequence by the Lyoncross Limestone, the Orchard Beds, the Calmy Limestone and the Castlecary Limestone at the top (River North Esk Excursion). Dominantly fluviatile conditions in the succeeding *Passage Group* produced thick coarse-grained, feldspathic sandstones as in the Roslin Sandstone of Midlothian (River North Esk Excursion). In West Lothian thick leached soils left valuable economic fireclays (River Avon Excursion). During the Namurian thick teschenite sills were intruded which, because of their hardness, form prominent landmarks as at Salisbury Crags, Gullane Hill, Mons Hill (Arthur's Seat, Gosford and South Queensferry-Cramond Excursions) and are commonly quarried for roadstone and aggregate.

The start of *Westphalian* or *Coal Measures* times heralded a widespread return to tropical forests and left an heritage of thick workable coal seams. Marine incursions provided marker bands which are used for correlation into Lower, Middle and Upper Coal Measures (equivalent to Westphalian A, B and C). By the *Stephanian* the climate had become semi-arid. No deposits remain but deep weathering extended down into the Upper Coal Measures strata, reddening the rocks and destroying many coal seams. Also about this time the Midland Valley quartz-dolerite sill was intruded along with the suite of W-E trending quartz-dolerite dykes, as seen at Hound Point and Dalmahoy Hill (South Queensferry-Cramond, Garleton Hills and Dunbar Excursions).

Following the Carboniferous there was a major mountain-building event, the *Hercynian Orogeny*, which folded the rocks into gentle anticlines and basins such as the Midlothian and East Lothian coalfields. Some of the major faults associated with the folding trend SW-NE, as the Colinton, Pentland and Crossgatehall faults, and others trend W-E, as the Murieston, Middleton Hall and Ochiltree faults. Long epochs followed without any local record of the geological history. The region was land subject to erosion, with desert conditions during the Permian and Triassic eras, more amenable climates during Jurassic, Cretaceous and Tertiary times as southerly seas covered most of England. Late in the Tertiary era the east-flowing drainage pattern of Scotland formed on an east tilted slope, giving rise to the Forth and its main north-east-flowing consequent streams.

During the last million years, in the *Quaternary* or *Pleistocene*, the region has been affected by several ice ages. Ice built up in the southern Highlands and the Southern Uplands, merged in the Midland Valley and flowed eastwards across the Lothian Region, deflected to ENE by the Pentlands, Moorfoots and Lammermuirs. As the ice ground down the rocks it moulded the landscape along its direction of flow. This resulted in rock surfaces striated by rock-laden ice, in crag-and-tail features such as Edinburgh Castle and the Royal Mile (The Castle Hill and Blackford Hill Excursions) and in drumlins, oval-shaped mounds formed of till (boulder clay). Till, which blankets most of the low ground in the region, is the ground moraine of the ice-sheet and consists of rounded pebbles and boulders in a grey, brown or red silty or sandy clay. The matrix and the clasts are mostly of local origin varying according to the bedrock, but erratics from further afield, such as Highland schists, are also found.

Fifteen thousand years ago the ice-sheet began to melt and break up. The Pentland, Moorfoot and Lammermuir Hills became ice-free while valley glaciers and stagnating ice-sheets still occupied low ground. Meltwater from the ice cut numerous glacial drainage channels, many of which now form dry valleys. Some channels follow the contours where meltwater flowed along ice margins, other channels form steep chutes where the meltwater escaped under the ice. The most spectacular dry valleys cut across watersheds, as in the Pentland Hills from Bavelaw to Flotterstone (The Pentland Hills Excursion), and in the Lammermuir Hills at Aikengall

(Lammermuir Deans Excursion). Glacial meltwater, eroding both till and bedrock, deposited gravels and sands as mounds, ridges and terraces, close to the ice margins. Silts and clays were deposited as lake alluvium or in estuaries and inlets of the sea, which then lay well above its present level.

Sea-levels fluctuated during and after the glaciation because of the trapping of sea-water into ice-sheets and isostatic adjustment of the land in response to the weight of the ice-sheet. The late-Glacial sea-level of the Forth ranged from over 30 m OD in the west to about 15 m OD in the east, whereas the main post-Glacial shoreline lies below 10 m OD, and forms extensive beach deposits with a prominent cliff at the back.

Lowering sea-levels rejuvenated rivers, and these cut gorges. River alluvium of gravel, sand, silt and clay was deposited in river terraces and flood-plains. Tides and longshore currents constantly transport and redeposit marine alluvium along the coasts.

Major alterations by man of the countryside bequeathed by nature include quarrying for limestone, aggregate, sand and gravel and other minerals; construction of bings of spent oil-shale and coal waste, and road and rail embankments; and reclamation of intertidal flats.

Maps

British Geological Survey maps are available for the whole region. Published 1:50 000 or 1:63 360 (*) maps can be purchased from BGS at Murchison House, West Mains Road, Edinburgh, EH9 3LA, or from Ordnance Survey stockists:

* Sheet 31	Airdrie	(Solid)
* Sheet 31	Airdrie	(Drift)
Sheet 32W	Livingston	(Solid)
Sheet 32E	Edinburgh	(Solid)
* Sheet 32	Edinburgh	(Drift)
Sheet 33W	Haddington	(Solid)
Sheet 33W	Haddington	(Drift)
Sheet 33E	Dunbar	(Solid)
Sheet 33E	Dunbar	(Drift)
Sheet 34	Eyemouth	(Solid)
Sheet 34	Eyemouth	(Drift)

There is also an Edinburgh Special Sheet (Solid and Drift) on the scale of 1:25 000. Geological maps with complete coverage of the region at 1:10 560 (six-inch) scale may be consulted at the British Geological Survey.

Publications

THE GEOLOGY OF SCOTLAND gives an introduction to Scottish Geology. The third editions of the BGS regional geology, THE MIDLAND VALLEY OF SCOTLAND and THE SOUTH OF SCOTLAND, provide a more detailed account. A recent sheet memoir is available for Sheet 32 (Edinburgh) and others are in preparation. A selection of the many books available as introductory reading on the various aspects of geology is included with the References at the end of this guide.

GEOLOGICAL CODE OF CONDUCT

THE Geological Code is reproduced here as a reminder to all that geological outcrops not only belong to the landowner but are an irreplaceable heritage for everyone. There is a delicate balance between geological conservation and the need to study rocks in their natural environment. Some outcrops are unique, irreplaceable, self-evident, and often rightly protected. Other outcrops in shores, cliff and quarries have an abundance of material available for hammering and collecting. The authors ask the readers of this guide to follow the code. In particular, leave outcrops in the state you would expect to find them and maintain good relations with landowners so that other geologists may be welcome.

(Drafted by the Geologists' Association and supported by all Geological Societies in Britain)

In recent years there has been a rapid increase in geological field studies, which are inevitably concentrated on a finite number of important rock outcrops. Sheer collecting pressure is destroying the scientific value of an increasing number of sites, many of them irreplaceable. At the same time the volume of field work has caused concern to many site owners.

A code of conduct has, therefore, become essential if the quality of field facilities is not to deteriorate still further. Geologists must show themselves responsible users of the countryside.

General

1. Always seek permission in advance to enter private land.
2. Obey the Country Code (e.g. shut gates, leave no litter).
3. Do not allow rock waste to spread on to agricultural land, where it may result in injury to animals, or on to roadways, where a hazard may be caused to pedestrians and vehicles.
4. Do not interfere with machinery or other property.
5. Avoid courting danger to yourself and others from such hazards as an insecure cliff or rock face. Take care to prevent the dislodging of rock which might fall on people beneath. Never place yourself in danger if climbing cliffs or other rock faces.
6. No rock face should be left in a state more dangerous than when you arrived.
7. Exercise the standard precautions when working in mountainous and remote areas, e.g. inform someone of your intended route.
8. Do not explore underground unless you have the proper experience and equipment.
9. On coastal sections, make sure you know the local tide conditions.

Visiting Quarries

1. Both arrival and departure must be reported. Make sure you have discussed with the manager or foreman where you may go and what local hazards to avoid.
2. The leader of a party should have visited the quarry in advance and must ensure that members do not become dispersed and out of sight.
3. Keep clear of vehicles and machinery and ensure you understand blast-warning procedures. Avoid sludge lagoons.

Collecting and Field Parties

1. Students should be trained to observe and record with sketches and photographs rather than to destroy by hammering.
2. Leaders of field-meeting parties should instruct their members not to carry hammers except for use in the working portion of a quarry where permission has been given, in a waste tip or on fallen blocks and scree.
3. Never collect from stone walls and buildings. Do not undermine fences, walls, bridges or other property.
4. When collecting, take the minimum material necessary and avoid removing fossils, mineral or rock specimens from *in situ* outcrops unless they are to be used for serious study.
5. Collecting from educational purposes should only be carried out where there is a large supply of common fossils.
6. The use of replicas of fossils is commended for teaching purposes.
7. The leader of a field party should remember that he bears responsibility for ensuring that the spirit of this code is fulfilled. This may oblige him to remind his party of the need for care and consideration at all times and require him to act as supervisor when his own inclination might be to study and collect.

The Research Worker

1. No research worker has a special right to 'dig out' a site in the name of science. If you have to collect, leave some of the material intact—new research techniques may be available to future generations of geologists.
2. Special excavations should be backfilled where necessary to safeguard against creating a hazard to men and animals and, where required, to protect vulnerable outcrops from casual collecting.
3. Avoid the disfigurement of rock surfaces with brightly coloured numbers and symbols in public places.
4. By lodging them with a responsible institution, ensure that your research material and notebooks become available for posterity.

Societies, Universities and Schools

1. Foster an interest in geological sites and their wise conservation. Much may be done to help clean up overgrown sites (with permission of the owner and in consultation with the Nature Conservancy Council).
2. Create working groups for those amateurs who wish to do field work and collect, so that leadership is available to direct their studies and ensure that their specimens are effectively logged and housed.
3. Join your local County Naturalists' Trusts, as individuals or as groups, to ensure that effective action is taken to protect the sites you use.

Publication

1. Take care that publicity does not lead to the destruction of vulnerable exposures. Where possible, without detriment to the scientific argument, avoid giving the precise locality of such sites. Help promote the establishment of a restricted access data centre where the details of such localities can be lodged.
2. It is requested that authors of introductory, educational and similar texts should draw attention to, or quote, the Code.

Landowners

1. It is suggested that landowners should ascertain that visiting geologists and party leaders are familiar with this Code.
2. In the event of abuse of the Code, landowners are requested to take the name and address of the individual or party leader and the Institution or Society to which he belongs. Such cases could be referred to the Association through its librarian.

ARTHUR'S SEAT

O.S. 1:50000 Sheet 66 Edinburgh
B.G.S. 1:50000 Sheet 32E Edinburgh
B.G.S. 1:25000 Edinburgh Special Sheet
Route: Map 3

ABOUT a kilometre from the city centre, the remnants of the long-extinct volcano of Arthur's Seat rise from the low ground on which Edinburgh is built. Part of the volcano has been lost through erosion and part has been buried under younger rocks; enough, however, is exposed to allow us to study the vulcanicity in some detail, especially as the removal of much of the superstructure has laid bare the internal parts of the volcano. The largest volcanic remnant lies within the Holyrood Park where it culminates in Arthur's Seat (251 m), the hill from which the volcano takes its name. To the north and west smaller remnants build the Calton Hill and the Castle Rock (p. 52). The volcano was active in the Dinantian, early in the Carboniferous Period, and the products of its first eruption are taken to mark the top of the Cementstone Group. The lavas are covered by the oldest sedimentary member of the succeeding Lower Oil-Shale Group, the Abbeyhill Shales.

The first eruption of the Arthur's Seat Volcano was made into shallow water in which the rocks of the Cementstone Group had accumulated, but, early in the activity, the higher parts of the cone were raised above water-level and colonised by land plants. Their fossilised remains are found to-day in the ashes and agglomerates. The deposition of chemically precipitated limestone high on the cone in the middle stages of the activity, and the final burial of the entire volcano by waterlaid sediment, indicate that the greater part of the cone was submerged during most of the volcano's life; this contention is supported by the presence locally of well-bedded ashes between most the lava flows. Thus, although the lavas were erupted subaerially, much of their descent of the cone was made below water. No trace of pillow structure, however, has ever been observed, but some of the higher lavas have been partially albitised and carbonated and are now transitional between normal basalts and spilites.

As exposed to-day, the Arthur's Seat Volcano consists of five vents (the composite Lion's Head and Lion's Haunch vents, the basalt-filled Castle Rock and Pulpit Rock vents and the agglomerate-filled Crags Vent), three portions of the cone (the Whinny and Calton Hills and an area near Duddingston) and a number of sills and dykes. The Salisbury Crags Sill and two small dykes were intruded long after the volcano became extinct.

Whinny Hill provides the most complete and accessible sequence of lavas. Lava 1, believed from petrographic evidence to have been erupted from the Castle Rock Vent, forms the Long Row and its northern downfaulted portion, the Haggis Knowe. Above the lava there lies a considerable thickness of mixed ash and sediment known collectively as the Lower Ash of the Dry Dam; this contains at least two bands of precipitated limestone, the lower containing irregular masses of chert. The ash, most probably derived from the Lion's Head Vent, is covered by Lava 2 which was erupted from the same orifice within which its feeding conduit is preserved. There followed the formation of a further bed of intermingled ash and sediment in which volcanic bombs are prominent—the Upper Ash of the Dry Dam. After the accumulation of the ash, a parasitic vent—the Pulpit Rock Vent—some distance down the northern slopes of the cone, emitted Lava 3. Later Lava 4 was erupted from the Lion's Head Vent at the apex of the cone and descended normally until diverted around the obstacle formed by Lava 3. Lava 4 is only seen on the southern part of Whinny Hill to-day, its northern continuation having been diverted out of the present plane of exposures by Lava 3. Lava 4 was the last flow to be erupted from the Lion's Head Vent for the residue of the flow remaining in the vent blocked the orifice on consolidation. All further activity of the Arthur's Seat Volcano was focused on the Lion's Haunch Vent from which the remaining nine lavas (5 to 13) of Whinny Hill were erupted. These flows lie in normal succession, one above

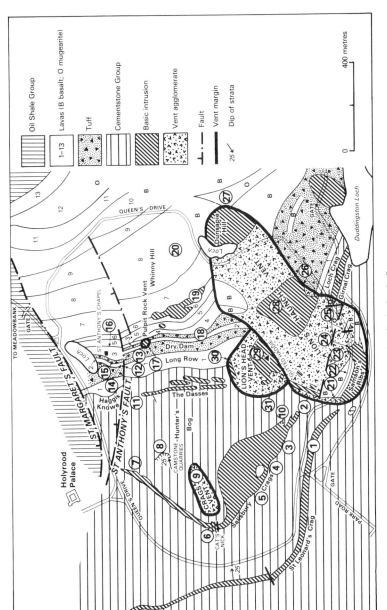

Map 3. Arthur's Seat

another, the contacts of the flows being rarely marked by any considerable ash bed.

The remnant of the cone of the Arthur's Seat Volcano exposed on the northern shores of Duddingston Loch differs extensively from the remnant which forms Whinny Hill and, apart from Lava 1, the successions cannot be correlated with any certainty. The Calton Hill succession (Locality 32) shows a general resemblance to that of the Whinny Hill.

Of the five vents of the volcano, that of the Lion's Haunch is by far the largest and most complex. It is filled chiefly by a red agglomerate consisting of a fine-grained red matrix of decomposed basaltic ash in which lie basaltic and sedimentary blocks up to 3 m in length. Within the agglomerate there occur at least seven small lava flows, of basalt or mugearite, which were erupted and confined within the crater walls. A common associate of these flows is a bedded red tuffaceous sandstone, pointing to the existence of temporary crater lakes during periods of quiescence in the vulcanicity. A mass of Dunsapie basalt forms the summit of the Lion's Haunch and partly rests on and partly cuts across the underlying agglomerate. This mass is the remnant of a one-time lava lake which probably once filled and blocked the Lion's Haunch Vent and brought the surface activity of the volcano to a close.

Several basaltic intrusions lie in the Lion's Haunch Vent. In the east there occurs the marginal intrusion of Dunsapie Hill, the type locality for Dunsapie basalt. In the west of the vent there crops out at Samson's Ribs an intrusion, again of Dunsapie basalt, which ascended along the wall of the vent and extended in a number of irregular tongues into the crater infilling.

The other three vents seen in the Holyrood Park are simpler in constitution. The Lion's Head Vent, now partly truncated by the later and larger Lion's Haunch Vent, appears to have been originally cylindrical in form and largely infilled by a fine agglomerate, through which penetrated the feeding conduits for Lavas 2 and 4; these conduits are now filled by Craiglockhart and Dalmeny basalt respectively. The Pulpit Rock Vent—the orifice of Lava 3—is a small plug of Craiglockhart basalt. The Crags Vent is filled with fine-grained agglomerate containing fragments of basalt similar to Lavas 1 and 2 of Whinny Hill. No higher flows have contributed fragments and it is probable that this vent ceased its activity shortly after the eruption of Lava 2.

The intrusions associated with the vulcanicity, other than those in the vents, include a sill, which has been divided into three portions now forming the St. Leonard's Crag, the Dasses and the Girnal Crag. The probable feeder of the sill is situated at the Dasses where some dyke-like contacts may be seen. A second sill, known as the Whinny Hill Intrusion, occurs between Lavas 6 and 7.

Two intrusions of later date than the Arthur's Seat vulcanicity occur in the Holyrood Park. The larger is the well-known teschenite sill of the Salisbury Crags of Namurian age. To the north of the Cat's Nick the sill is cut by a later (Stephanian) quartz-dolerite dyke which contains a large strip xenolith of the sill rock.

After the final extinction of the volcano it was covered by thousands of feet of sediments. Earth-movements folded the strata and imparted to the buried Arthur's Seat Volcano a general eastward dip of between 20° and 30°. Many faults cut the sediments and the volcanic rocks. The sedimentary cover of the volcano was removed by prolonged denudation which culminated in the distinctive erosion caused by the Pleistocene ice-sheet. The ice moved from west to east across the area; the hard rocks of the Arthur's Seat Volcano were left as high land while the soft surrounding sediments were more extensively planed away. The easterly dip of the volcanic rocks caused the ice-sheet to produce the present-day topography of westward facing cliffs backed by gentle easterly slopes. The famous crag-and-tail structure of the Castle Rock and the High Street is the best known of these phenomena, but similar land forms have been produced at the Salisbury Crags and the Calton Hill. A fine *roche moutonnée* has been preserved in the Queen's Drive and glacial striae can be observed at several localities.

The great majority of the geological phenomena to be seen on Arthur's Seat can be adequately appreciated without hammering the outcrops. As the area is intensively used by geologists for field studies, it is requested that visitors use their hammers as sparingly as possible. At a number of outcrops, including localities 3 and 15 below, hammering is strictly forbidden by the Park Authorities.

Four excursions are described in detail. These, with their approximate duration, are:

		Time
A	Salisbury Crags	2½ hrs
B	Whinny Hill	3 hrs
C	Lion's Head and Lion's Haunch Vents	3 hrs
D	Calton Hill	1 hr

Holyrood Park lies to the centre of Edinburgh and Lothian Region Transport buses pass close to all three park gates. Ample parking for cars is available inside the Holyrood and Meadowbank gates and at Dunsapie Loch, but parking is difficult at the Park Road gate. The Park Authorities should be advised in advance of large parties. Prior permission is required to take coaches into the park and they may not park there. Note that the eastern half of the Queen's Drive, from Meadowbank Gate to Park Road Gate, has been converted to oneway driving.

Excursion A—Salisbury Crags (Figure 6)

Fig 6. Salisbury Crags

Access to the Holyrood Park is gained by the Park Road Gate and localities 1 to 10 visited in succession. Alternatively from the Holyrood car park the localities can be visited in the order 8 to 10 followed by 1 to 7.

1. St. Leonard's Crag

In a low interrupted line of cliffs to the south of the Queen's Drive the St. Leonard's Sill is exposed. The central member of Dunsapie basalt, seen elsewhere, is absent and the sill, about 5 m in thickness, consists throughout of a brownish-red, markedly altered mugearite containing sparse plagioclase phenocrysts and small vesicles.

2. Queen's Drive: Cementstone Group

On the north side of the Queen's Drive white or pale red sandstones and marls are exposed. Several tons of rock were blasted from this exposure and removed for examination: several fish scales were found and were originally identified as *Holoptychius nobilissimus* suggesting that the strata were of Upper Old Red Sandstone age. Re-investigations have cast doubt on this identification and Mitchell and Mykura (1962) put forward strong evidence that the rocks seen in this outcrop belong to the Cementstone Group.

3. Salisbury Crags: Hutton's Section

The justly famous Hutton's Section of the base of Salisbury Crags Sill is found towards the south-eastern end of the escarpment, and provided Hutton and his followers with telling evidence in favour of magmatic intrusion in the great argument with the Wernerians in the eighteenth century. Beneath the sill lie well-bedded Cementstone Group strata, alternately red and white. The sill transgresses the bedding conspicuously in two places. At the first the sediment against the transgression is crumpled; at the other a wedge of teschenite has been intruded beneath a block of sediment, rotating it upwards from its original position and partly engulfing it in the sill. At the western end of the section, the teschenite immediately above the contact has been chilled to a glassy skin up to a centimetre thick, which has now been devitrified to a greenish material. Above the glass the teschenite is very fine in grain but coarsens markedly upwards. In the rock-face to the south-east of Hutton's section large rafts of sediment can be seen high in the sill. The rafts are not distorted and lie parallel to the strata below the sill. Still farther to the south-west, syenitic segregation veins up to 5 cm in thickness cut the sill.

4. Hutton's Rock

At the north-western end of the largest disused quarry in the Salisbury Crags Sill, a small isolated rock stands close to

FIG 7. Hutton's Rock

the path. Owing its preservation to the interest of Hutton, it is now known as Hutton's Rock (Figure 7). Here teschenite which has been extensively hematitised is cut by a vein of impure hematite several centimetres in thickness.

5. Sill-Sandstone Relations

Here, at the foot of the Salisbury Crags, a mass of red sandstone is bordered above and on the east by the sill. Its other contacts are not seen and it is therefore uncertain whether it is a true xenolith or a tongue of the underlying sediments projecting into the sill. The intrusion of the sill has crumpled the sandstone and has locally produced slight faulting.

6. Cat's Nick: Fault, Quartz-dolerite Dyke

At the Cat's Nick a small east-west fault with a downthrow of a metre or so to the north cuts the Salisbury Crags Sill and the underlying sediments. The teschenite close to the fault is much decomposed and shows spheroidal weathering. A few metres farther to the north, a quartz-dolerite dyke traverses the sill. The dyke, about a metre in width, is much finer in grain than the sill and shows a distinct joint pattern. Just above the path it contains a large strip-xenolith of teschenite.

7. Sill: Upper Contact

In a prominent embayment into the line of the Crags, the upper contact of the teschenite sill is exposed. The teschenite decreases markedly in granularity and becomes vesicular as the contact is approached; the sediments above, white sandstones of the Cementstone Group, show little alteration other than a slight induration.

8. Camstone Quarries: Cementstone Group Sediments

In the disused Camstone Quarries sandstones, shales and cementstones of the Cementstones Group dip eastwards at 25°. Well developed sun-cracks, ripple-marks and worm-tracks occur and from the cementstones the small crustacean *Estheria peachi* has been obtained.

9. Crags Vent: Agglomerate

A low mound marks the position of the Crags Vent and is bounded by a very broken scrap in which the fine-grained agglomerate of the vent is exposed.

10. Sill: Upper Contact, Tachylyte Veins

At the top of the main cliff of the Salisbury Crags, the teschenite sill very close to its upper contact is exposed and is seen to contain vesicles which, in places, are arranged in trains as a result of late magmatic movement. Patches of altered sediment, of Cementstone age, lie upon the teschenite a few metres east of the Crags and the teschenite here is locally cut by veins of dark tachylyte. To the south and east of this locality the sill splits up into a number of leaves separated by thin layers of intervening sediment.

Excursion B—Whinny Hill

The approach to Whinny Hill for localities 11 to 20 is most easily made from the western end of St. Margaret's Loch which can be conveniently reached from either the Holyrood or Meadowbank Gates car parks.

11. Dasses Sill

The sill of the Dasses here forms a low westward facing cliff. Only a metre or so in thickness, it consists of highly altered Markle basalt transitional to mugearite. The top of the sill is well-exposed and shows a number of north-west—south-east corrugations, representing casts of drag-folds in the overlying sediments caused by the movement of the magma. A few centimetres of very slightly indurated sediment can be seen above the sill and directly below the turf at the eastern margin of the outcrop.

12. Long Row: Lava 1

The Dunsapie basalt which forms Lava 1 is well-exposed at the northern termination of the Long Row. The base of the flow is not seen but the greater part of its thickness is exposed. The flow is sparsely vesicular throughout and the central part shows a crude columnar jointing. The irregular and slaggy top of the flow is exposed in the path leading to the Dry Dam almost where it joins the path uphill past St. Anthony's Well; the irregularities in the top of the lava are filled with basaltic ash.

13. St. Anthony's Well: Lower Ash of the Dry Dam

The Lower Ash of the Dry Dam is somewhat poorly exposed at this locality. Above the top of Lava 1 there crops out a bed of white limestone, a metre thick. The limestone contains cherty nodules and is associated with dark sandy shales containing plant remains. In the small scrape on the south side of the path leading past St. Anthony's Well, ashy and shaly beds are exposed and are overlain by another impure limestone. Lava 2, which overlies the Lower Ash, is not exposed at this locality on the south side of the St. Anthony's Fault.

14. St. Anthony's Well: Lava 2

This locality lies to the north of the path running to the east past St. Anthony's Well and is the lowest westward facing cliff on the slope below St. Anthony's Chapel. The well lies on the east-west St. Anthony's Fault so that Locality 14 is separated from Localities 13 and 12 by this dislocation; the fault has thrown the rocks down to the north by some 23 m. At Locality 14 Lava 2 crops out. The flow, of Craiglockhart basalt, is of no great thickness and is decomposed and vesicular throughout. At the south-western extremity of the exposure the flow has been gas-brecciated, the fragments now being cemented by calcite. The upper surface of Lava 2 is irregular, the irregularities being filled with ash or sediment.

15. Lava 2: Upper Ash of the Dry Dam

The upper surface of Lava 2 forms a small ledge in the westward facing cliff below St. Anthony's Chapel. Above and to the east of the ledge the ash is exposed and is covered by the columnar basal portion of Lava 3. The metre-thick ash is well-bedded and contains occasional volcanic bombs up to 0·7 m in diameter. Near its base the ash carries numerous coalified plant fragments; a tooth of *Rhizodus* and remains of *Elonichthys striatus* and *Callopristodus pectinatus* have been found here.

16. St. Anthony's Chapel: Lava 3

Lava 3 is a basalt of Craiglockhart type and the lower part, seen around the ruins of St. Anthony's Chapel, is markedly columnar, the individual columns being about 0·7 m in diameter and inclined steeply to the west. Some 5 m above the base of the flow the markedly columnar portion grades into an irregularly columnar portion which is exposed locally at the base of the cliffs to the east of the Chapel. This, in turn, passes very gradually upwards into the topmost zone of the lava—an assemblage of basaltic blocks lying in a matrix of identical composition. The blocky portion has a marked pyroclastic appearance and most probably originated by the brecciation of the cold crust of the lava by the movement of the still liquid interior. The blocky portion is about 15 m thick. The total thickness of the flow exceeds 25 m.

17. Pulpit Rock: Basalt Plug, Lavas 2, 4

The small parasitic vent of the Pulpit Rock is occupied by a plug of Craiglockhart basalt which forms a prominent cliff high on the eastern slopes of the Dry Dam. Columnar jointing is well-developed, the columns being curved; in the centre of the mass they are more or less vertical but, on being traced towards the margin, the individual columns approach the horizontal, indicating that they have been chilled against the vertical wall of the vent. To the south of the cliff the contact of the plug with Lava 2 is exposed, the lava being much altered in proximity to the junction. Lava 4, which to the south forms the cliff along the eastern wall of the Dry Dam, also comes into contact with the Pulpit Rock Vent but, being younger, naturally shows no increase of alteration at the contact. The connection between Lava 3 and its feeder—the plug in the Pulpit Rock Vent—is still preserved and may be traced on the north side of the vent.

18. Dry Dam: Upper Ash, Lavas 2, 4, 5, 6

At this locality the Upper Ash of the Dry Dam is exposed in a number of outcrops. Its base can be observed resting on Lava 2 and its top seen to be covered by Lava 4 which here forms the cliff immediately to the east of the Dry Dam. The ash here is coarse, especially in its upper part, and contains numerous ejected blocks and bombs of basalt.

Between Localities 18 and 19, Lavas 4, 5 and 6 can be examined. The foremost is a Dalmeny type basalt, the latter two are of Jedburgh type.

19. Whinny Hill Intrusion

Whinny Hill Intrusion, a small sill, lies between Lavas 6 and 7. The two flows are microporphyritic Jedburgh basalts and present a strong contrast in appearance to the markedly macroporphyritic Craiglockhart basalt of the sill. The sill lies along a hollow between the dip slope of Lava 6 to the west and the scarp of Lava 7 to the east. The feeding pipe of the intrusion cuts Lava 5, another Jedburgh basalt, 45 m to the south-west of the northern extremity of the sill outcrop.

20. Whinny Hill: Lavas 7, 8–10

The return route from Locality 19 lies at first eastwards across the dip slope of Whinny Hill. Here exposures of Lavas 7 (Jedburgh), 8, 9 and 10 (all Markle) can be seen. On reaching the Queen's Drive the road is followed northwards and westwards; roadside exposures of the same flows can be examined in descending order.

The Park can be left either at the Meadowbank or the Holyrood gates.

Excursion C—Lion's Haunch and Lion's Head Vents (Figure 8)

Access to localities 21 to 31 can be made by the Park Road Gate, or from the Dunsapie Loch car park visiting localities 27 to 31 then 21 to 26.

Fig 8. Arthur's Seat

21. Queen's Drive: Samson's Ribs Crater Lavas

The Samson's Ribs crater lavas, exposed in the Queen's Drive, dip towards the centre of the Lion's Haunch Vent. The lowest flow is brecciated throughout and has a slaggy top overlain by a foot of red tuffaceous sandstone. Above comes another lava, again with a slaggy upper surface, and this is in turn succeeded by a third flow. Above this uppermost flow lies the main mass of crudely bedded agglomerate of the Lion's Haunch Vent.

22. Roche moutonnée, Glacial Striae

From the retaining wall on the north side of the Queen's Drive there protrudes a *roche moutonnée*. The rock is striated horizontally, the striations tending to narrow towards the east; some plucking of the eastern end of the mass has occurred. The direction and narrowing of the striations, and the plucking, all point to the existence of a stream of ice moving from west to east through the hollow now occupied by the Queen's Drive. A few yards to the east a slickensided surface occurs by the roadside and can be contrasted with the glaciated surface.

23 and 24. Samson's Ribs Intrusion, Agglomerate

A small exposure of columnar Dunsapie basalt occurs on the north side of the Queen's Drive above the retaining wall. The columns, some 20 cm across, plunge southwards. The exposure marks the north-eastern termination of the Samson's Ribs Intrusion, which here cuts the agglomerate overlying the Samson's Ribs crater lavas farther to the west. The main part of the intrusion, which is markedly columnar in nature, is best seen in the cliff below to the Queen's Drive.

The north side of the Queen's Drive is here (24) marked by a cliff of coarse agglomerate containing abundant basalt blocks and a lesser proportion of blocks of sedimentary rocks. The basalt blocks are of Dunsapie or Markle type. The matrix in which the blocks lie is a red decomposed basaltic ash.

25. Crater Lavas and Ash

In the cliff above the Queen's Drive a crater lava of Jedburgh basalt rests on a few metres of ashy sediment which, in turn, lie on agglomerate; the lava and sediment dip towards the north-east at a moderate angle. A small north-south fault repeats the slaggy top of the flow and its covering of agglomerate. Approximately 90 m farther to the north-east, a crater of lava of mugearite is seen in the cliff above the Queen's Drive. This flow is covered by ashy sediments which are themselves overlain by agglomerate; the dip of the flow is again towards the north-east. Several small north-south faults cut this mugearite flow.

26. Loch Crag: Vent Margin, Lava 1, Limestone

The southern margin of the Lion's Haunch Vent is exposed above the retaining wall of the Queen's Drive where it can be seen truncating Lava 1 and the sediments and ashes above and below that flow. The lava forms a low southward facing cliff which can be followed upwards for a short distance from the road until it is cut across by the vent. The actual contact is not seen but can be fixed to within a metre or so. At this point the feeder of the Lion's Haunch Basalt occurs at the vent wall so that the contact is between the sparsely porphyritic Dunsapie basalt of the lava and the highly porphyritic Dunsapie basalt of the feeder. Sediments of the Cementstone Group have been seen below the lava; they are truncated by the vent and lie against agglomerate. Above the lava ash and sediments are visible; they are cut across by the vent which here also contains agglomerate.

Blocks of a white limestone, identical to a bed seen *in situ* some feet above the lava, are found sparsely throughout the agglomerates at this locality.

27. Dunsapie Hill: Intrusion, Mugearite Lava

To the east of Dunsapie Hill, a mugearite lava forms a number of small outcrops. The rock is pale purplish-grey and is cut by numerous platy joints. It lies above a Markle flow exposed farther to the south. Both flows are cut by the Dunsapie Hill Intrusion within the Lion's Haunch Vent.

28. Lion's Haunch Basalt

The highly-porphyritic Lion's Haunch Basalt, the remains of a lava-lake resting on the agglomerate which forms the chief infilling of the Lion's Haunch Vent, is well seen in numerous exposures at this locality.

29. Lion's Head Basalt, Viewpoint

The summit of Arthur's Seat—the Lion's Head—is formed of a glacially moulded basaltic plug which acted as the feeder for Lava 4 and which, on consolidation, blocked the Lion's Head Vent. From the summit the chief geological features of the Lothians and Fife can be clearly seen.

30 and 31. Lion's Head Vent Margin, Agglomerate

This locality lies at the junction of the Lion's Head Vent and Lava 1. On tracing the lava southwards, it becomes shattered and altered close to the vent and its dip increases from less than 20° to 40°. The actual contact is not visible, but its position can be fixed within a metre. A dyke of Craig-lockhart basalt, the feeder of Lava 2, lies within the vent at the junction. On the slope above the dyke the fine agglomerate of the vent is exposed.

The agglomerate of the Lion's Head Vent is roughly bedded and has an inwards dip (31). It contains numerous small fragments of Dunsapie and Craiglockhart basalt but no fragments of Markle basalt occur. The small size of the fragments and the absence of Markle blocks distinguish this agglomerate from that of the Lion's Haunch Vent. A large gully, known as the Gutted Haddie, has been eroded along the line of contact between the Lion's Head and the Lion's

Haunch vents; some 15 m to the north of this gully a small basalt dyke cuts the Lion's Head Vent.

The return from this excursion can be made either by the Hunter's Bog to the Holyrood Gate or through the low col between the Salisbury Crags and the Lion's Haunch to the Holyrood Park Road Gate.

Excursion D—Calton Hill

The Calton Hill succession may be easily followed by ascending the steps at the east end of Waterloo Place (NT 261 741) and proceeding eastwards over the hill.

32. Calton Hill: Lavas and Ashes

At the base of the succession alternations of ash and sediment occur. These represent the two ash beds of the Dry Dam, for the equivalents of Lavas 1 and 2 of the Whinny Hill are not found on the Calton Hill. Above the ashes lie two lavas of Craiglockhart basalt, the lower closely resembling Lava 3 of the Whinny Hill. Lavas 4, 5, 6 and 7 of the Whinny Hill are not found, their temporal equivalent being a thick bed of ash containing an unsorted assemblage of boulders, blocks and bombs of basalt. Above this there lies a group of three lavas of Markle basalt separated by thin ash-beds—the local equivalents of Lavas 8, 9 and 10 of the Whinny Hill. On the highest Markle flow lies another ash-bed which, in turn, is overlain by a group of three mugearite lavas, again separated by ash-beds; these flows are the approximate equivalents in time of Whinny Hill Lavas 11 and 12. The highest mugearite lava of the Calton Hill is directly covered by the Abbeyhill Shales.

G. P. BLACK

CITY OF EDINBURGH

O.S. 1:50000 Sheet 66 Edinburgh
B.G.S. 1:50000 Sheet 32E Edinburgh
B.G.S. 1:25000 Edinburgh Special Sheet
Route: Map 4

Two short itineraries illustrating features of geological interest near the city centre are described. Together with walking distance and approximate duration they are:

		Time	Walking Distance
A	The Dean	1½ hours	2 km
B	The Castle Hill	3½ hours	2 km

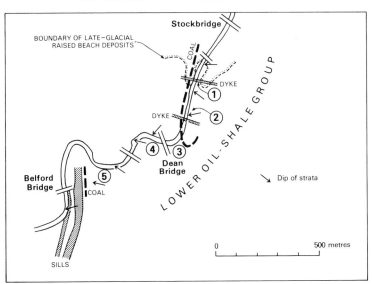

MAP 4. Water of Leith valley

A short note is also appended on the Royal Museum of Scotland.

49

Excursion A—The Dean

The excursion starts at Stockbridge (NT 246 746) reached by Lothian Region Transport bus from the city centre.

Between Drumsheugh and Stockbridge the Water of Leith has cut its course through the sandstones and shales of the Granton Sandstones, which belong to the Lower Oil-Shale Group. The valley exposes what is virtually a strike section of the beds which here dip westwards and occupy the west limb of the St. Andrew's Square Anticline which is an expression within the city of the Pentland Anticline. This anticline is followed to the west by the Granton-Wardie Syncline.

1. St. Bernard's Well: Granton Sandstones, Quartz-dolerite Dyke

Proceed to St. Bernard's Well (Figure 9) by way of Saunders Street, which follows the Water of Leith upstream from the bridge at Stockbridge, and the footpath by the waterside when the Dean Park is reached. St. Bernard's Well was a sulphurous medicinal well whose waters were prized for many years, as the classic 18th century well-house shows. In the river bank opposite the well, a quartz-dolerite dyke is exposed cutting shales and flaggy sandstones of the Granton Sandstones. The dyke is about 1 m in thickness and trends west-north-westwards.

Skirt the well by the waterside, and follow the path upstream for 25 m where a current-bedded sandstone with good ripple-marks is well seen dipping westwards.

2. St. George's Well: Sandstones, Dyke

Return to St. Bernard's Well, mount the steps to the main pathway and, turning right, follow the path upstream for 200 m when, in the river under a small building, St. George's Well, to the right of the path, another quartz-dolerite dyke cutting a bed of sandstone is exposed. This dyke is some 3 m in thickness and its trend is parallel to the St. Bernard's Well dyke.

A poor coal occurs in the river bed some 105 m above the second dyke and some 30 m downstream from the Dean Bridge. Unfortunately access to this coal is not possible.

Fig 9. St. Bernard's Well

3. The Dean Bridge: Shales in Granton Sandstones

Follow the path upstream for a further 30 m when on the left-hand side, in the cliff below the Dean Bridge, occurs a fine exposure of shales with ironstone nodules and sandstone above. It is possible to collect from the shales at this exposure where, in addition to plant, entomostracan and fish remains, *Naiadites obesus* (R. Eth. jnr.) has been obtained.

4. Miller Row: Granton Sandstones/Wardie Shales Junction

Passing under the Dean Bridge reach the ornamental mill-wheels in Miller Row. Here the Water of Leith occupies a westerly loop of its course and the shales and sandstones of the Granton Beds, which were seen at the last exposure to be dipping westwards at some 15°, plunge into the river bed and are succeeded on the opposite cliff, under the church building, by 55 m of bituminous shales. From fossil evidence obtained further along the strike at Drumsheugh, it is known that these bituminous shales belong to the succeeding Wardie Shales.

5. Dean Gorge: Post-Glacial Cut

From this viewpoint in Miller Row the post-glacial cut of the Dean gorge is well seen. Upstream from Belford Bridge the Water of Leith occupies a valley filled with deep boulder-clay which presumably represents its pre-glacial course. At Stockbridge the river meanders over the late-glacial Raised Beach deposits. At the Dean, however, the valley is steep-sided and cut in rock with no boulder-clay filling. It is probable that in post-glacial times the river was deflected from its original course by the resistant dolerite sills at Belford Bridge, causing the river, heavy with glacial melt-water and rejuvenated by the rising land level, to cut the spectacular gorge of Dean.

Follow Miller Row to the small bridge and, turning left, ascend Bell's Brae to Queensferry Road which leads to the West End of Princes Street.

Excursion B—The Castle Hill

The Excursion starts at the Half-Moon Battery (252 735) in the Castle. A Lothian Region Transport bus from Waverley Bridge goes up the Mound. Turn off at Johnston Terrace and go to the Lawnmarket.

1. Within the Castle Walls: Crag-and-Tail, Plug/Carboniferous Junction

The Castle Hill and the Royal Mile form a classic example of crag-and-tail featuring. The ice sheet moved from the west and impinged on the western face of the basaltic plug on which the Castle is built. Ice was deflected towards the north and excavated the valley now occupied by Princes Street Gardens and the railway line leading to Waverley Station.

Ice which was deflected to the south excavated the valley now occupied by the Grassmarket and the Cowgate. The 'tail' composed by sediments protected by the 'crag' and overlying drift, forms the gentle slope or the Royal Mile leading from the Castle to the Palace of Holyrood House. These features are well seen from the vantage points of the Half-Moon Battery and the Fore Well Battery.

The Fore Well, situated at the northern end of the Half-Moon Battery, marks the position of the junction of the basaltic plug with the lower Carboniferous sediments which lie to the east. The basalt may be seen at the summit of the Castle Hill between the National War Memorial and the Half-Moon Battery, which is itself built on sediments (see below). Descend by the steps adjoining Argyll's Tower and turning right pass through the Portcullis gate. Some 10 m short of the Inner Barrier the northern part of the eastern junction may be seen in the right-hand gutter of the roadway. Here the basalt and greenish-grey Carboniferous marl are exposed close together, the marl having been hardened by contact with the basalt. Continue down the roadway and on reaching the souvenir shop opposite the guardhouse look at the cliff behind it towards the Half-Moon Battery when it is possible to see the sediments upon which the Battery is built. They lie between the junction with the basaltic plug, and the Castle Fault to the east, and consist of greenish marly shales dipping very steeply inwards towards the basalt. This dip was beneficial in accumulating water for the Fore Well.

2. Johnston Terrace (251 734): Plug/Carboniferous Sediments Junction, Castle Fault

Leaving the Castle cross the Esplanade and descend the stairs to the right at Castle Wynd North. On reaching Johnston Terrace turn right and proceed downhill for 200 m. Above the grassy slope to the right, in the corner formed by the Half-Moon Battery and the Old Palace, the southern part of the eastern junction is well seen. It is vertical and the Castle Fault lies just to the east. The dip of the sediments near the junction is steep but the sandstones under the esplanade, which are to the east of the Castle Fault, are dipping gently away from the plug. Continuing down Johnston Terrace the margin of the basalt rises as a steep cliff. The basalt which composes it is microporphyritic and of Dalmeny type. In thin-section it shows small altered olivines and augites embedded in a mesh of felspar crystals with microlithic augite and magnetite granules. The natural appearance of the basalt in the cliff above Johnston Terrace, and in the cliff overlooking Princes Street Gardens on the north side of the plug, has been somewhat altered by grouting and rock-bolting to stabilise the cliff face.

3. West Princes Street Gardens: Plug/Carboniferous Sediments Junction, Glacial Striae

Follow the base of the Castle Rock by entering West Princes Street Gardens by the Gate on the right 20 m short of the bridge carrying Johnston Terrace over King's Stables Road. On the left of the footpath is the valley excavated by ice whose easterly movement has been arrested by the west face of the Castle Rock. Use has been made of this valley as a site for the Car Park entered from Castle Terrace. On the right of the footpath the western junction of the plug with the Carboniferous sediments may be followed. Where it is first seen the contact is with sandstone, then some 100 m to the north-west with sandstone and marl, and then another 30 m to the north with marly shales. Follow the footpath to the northern face of the Castle Rock where marginal chilling of the basalt is well displayed.

Glacial moulding may be seen at a height of some 5 m on the northern face of the plug where it most closely approaches the railway. Near the ruins of the Old Well House glacial striae occur with an approximately east-west orientation. Looking westwards from the Well House there is evidence in the plug of horizontal columnar jointing controlled by cooling against a vertical margin. These joints are radial in plan and, although best seen at this position, may be traced all round the outcrop of the plug.

The railway traverses the site of a post-glacial lake which occupied the ice-excavated valley between the Castle and Princes Street. Between A.D. 1450 and 1816 the site was occupied by a smaller artificial lake called the Nor' Loch.

Access to Princes Street may be gained by way of one of the footbridges which span the railway.

The Royal Museum of Scotland (258 733)

The Museum is situated in Chambers Street, which may be reached from Princes Street by way of the Mound and George IV Bridge or the East End and the Bridges. Opening hours are weekdays 1000 to 1700, Sundays 1400 to 1700.

The museum houses extensive geological collections, in particular Scottish minerals and Scottish fossils. In addition to displays of Scottish material there are exhibitions of a more general geological interest, to be seen in the Mineral Hall and the Evolution Exhibition.

C. D. WATERSTON

BUILDING STONES OF EDINBURGH

O.S. 1:50000 Sheet 66 Edinburgh
B.G.S. 1:50000 Sheet 32E Edinburgh
Route: Map 5

EDINBURGH is a city built of sandstone, both the Old Town of
narrow wynds and tenements clustered round the Castle and
the Royal Mile, and the planned New Town stretching north
from Princes Street in spacious streets, squares and terraces.
For the Old Town much of the building stone was pink and
purple sandstones of Upper Old Red Sandstone age,
quarried locally at Bruntsfield or Craigmillar. White and pale
grey sandstones in the Lower Oil-Shale Group around
Edinburgh became available for the New Town, particularly
Hailes Sandstone from Hailes and Redhall quarries, Craigleith Sandstone (Figure 10) and Ravelston Sandstone. The
advent of canal, rail and finally road transport allowed
stone to be carried from further afield, such as the yellow
Binny Sandstone in the Upper Oil-Shale Group from
Binny, Humbie and Dalmeny quarries in West Lothian,
Cullalo stone from sandstone quarries in a similar horizon
near Aberdour in Fife, and New Red desert sandstones
from Locharbriggs Quarry, near Dumfries, Corsehill
Quarry at Annan, and Moat Quarry near Carlisle. As
Scottish quarries closed, Lower Carboniferous sandstones
were brought from quarries in the north of England, e.g.
Doddington near Wooler, Prudham near Hexham, Blaxter
at Elsdon, Cragg at Bellingham and Darney at West
Woodburn. More recently, exotic stones, mainly polished,
including marbles, limestones and granites have been used
as 'geological wallpapers' on the steel-framed constructions
of the 20th century (Craig 1892). By the 1950's most of
Edinburgh's sandstone buildings were obscured by layers of
black grime, a legacy of household coal fires which earned
the capital city its nickname 'Auld Reekie'. In the past few
decades many buildings have been cleaned revealing their

Fɪɢ 10. Craigleith Quarry

original colours and the structures and textures of the building stones.

Building terms used in this account include:

architrave—the lowest horizontal member lying above a column in a
    colonnaded building
ashlar—hewn blocks of masonry finely dressed to size and laid in courses
cornice—the moulded ledge projecting along the top of a building or
    feature in a building
course—a continuous layer of stones of the same height in a building—
    stones laid in layers
dress—to work stone to a comparatively smooth surface
drove—to work stone to smooth face then finish with sharp horizontal tool
    marks
mullion—vertical division between the lights of a window
quoins—dressed stones at the angles of buildings
rock-faced—masonry worked to a rugged natural appearance, like natural
    rock
rusticated—treatment of joints in masonry giving a V-section chamferring
    or a square section channelling
rubble—masonry of stones in a rough state and of irregular shape and
    size, can be laid in courses or uncoursed (random)
sneck—small stone in squared rubble often used to make up bed for bond-
    ing—hence 'snecked rubble'

stugged—masonry which has been roughened with a pointed hammer to
    provide key for rendering
stucco—external smooth rendering of wall (literally plaster)

In a short walk from the Old Town near the top of the
Mound, by the first phase of the New Town, to the top of the
Calton Hill, a selection of the most widely used local and
exotic stone can be seen. Since this walk covers the busiest
parts of Edinburgh, it is recommended for during the quieter
evening traffic. Hand lenses could prove useful, but it goes
without saying that hammers are unnecessary.

Top of the Mound

The walk begins at the top of the Playfair Steps, poised
between Old and New Town. To the south is St James Court,
an eight storey double tenement (built 1723–27) typical of
the Old Town. The left half of the recently restored eastern
tenement, housing a small restaurant, is built in random
rubble, mostly pink, bedded Upper Old Red Sandstone, with
relieving arches over the windows. Offices occupy the right
half of the tenement which is similarly constructed, apart
from the western turret in an orange-coloured sandstone.
The western tenement, housing the Consistorial Department
of the Sheriff Court and the Free Church Offices, is markedly
different, having been rebuilt in 1860. Its greyish sandstone is
in coursed, squared, rock-faced snecked ashlar with decora-
tions in polished ashlar.

New College to the west is built in orange-coloured Binny
Sandstone. The stonework has a stugged finish, but the
pinnacled buttresses are in polished ashlar. The Bank of
Scotland (1806) to the east was possibly the first large building in Edinburgh to use Binny Sandstone.

The Mound itself was formed from cartloads of earth dug
from foundations for houses in the New Town, from 1783 on-
wards. Up to 1800 cartloads a day were dumped, allowing
passage for carriages up the completed earth path within
3 years. By 1791, 1·3 million loads had been dumped, and by
1830, 2 million loads—at no cost to the City!

Towards the west the attractive red sandstone building of
the recently cleaned Caledonian Hotel (1903) can be seen in
the middle distance. Use of Locharbriggs stone, brought in
from Dumfriesshire by the Caledonian Railway, became

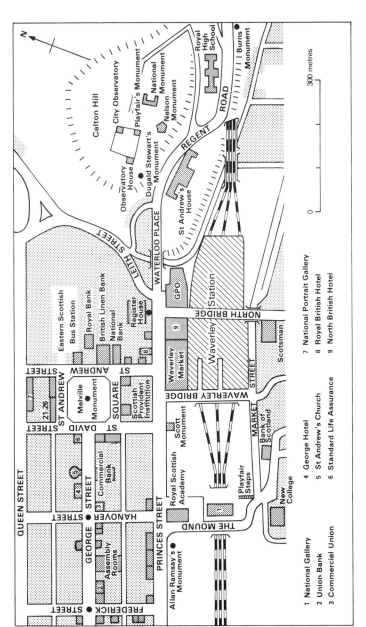

MAP 5. Edinburgh city centre

1 National Gallery
2 Union Bank
3 Commercial Union
4 George Hotel
5 St Andrew's Church
6 Standard Life Assurance
7 National Portrait Gallery
8 Royal British Hotel
9 North British Hotel

popular from the 1880s. It was an obvious choice for the company's Edinburgh terminus. The hotel is still open, but the railway station closed in 1965.

Foot of the Mound

Descent of the Playfair Steps gives access to two very important and recently cleaned buildings at the foot of the Mound. Both the more austere National Gallery and the Royal Scottish Academy to the north were designed by the architect William Playfair.

The National Gallery (begun in 1850) is built of Binny Sandstone brought the 20 km to Edinburgh by the Union Canal (opened 1822) which passed only 3 km from the main quarry near Uphall. Binny stone was fairly easy to work when fresh from the quarry but soon hardened on exposure to the air. It was said that a stone-worker could chisel 15 linear feet of Binny stone in the time it took him to dress 6 feet of Craigleith stone. Iron content produced the orange colour of Binny stone while bitumen gave it a freckled appearance and was believed to increase its durability. Ripple-marking and cross-bedding can be seen in the large polished ashlar blocks.

The Royal Scottish Academy was built as the Royal Institution in two stages. The original building (1822–6) is a mixture of polished Craigleith stone and Cullalo sandstone from Fife. The Board of Trustees for Manufacturers and Fisheries who held the feu accepted the lowest of five estimates which depended on the use of the softer, cheaper Cullalo stone, but harder, more expensive Craigleith stone had to be used when the Fife Quarry was unable to produce enough good quality stone. In extending the building (1831–6) Playfair doubled the columns in each colonade, elaborated the porticos at north and south ends and added a second row of columns and decorative detail to the Princes Street end pediment. This newer work, which stands out in the cleaned building, probably used Binny stone. The eight sphinxes carved by Sir John Steell and the statue of Queen Victoria seated in the robes of Britannia are known to be in this stone. Twice in its 150 years history the Royal Scottish Academy building has suffered failure of the wooden piles used as foundations on the 'mound' of earth. First in 1898 the north-west corner was affected, and in 1909 the north-east corner, leaving the edge of the roof on the west side looking uneven.

Almost opposite the Royal Scottish Academy, on the north side of Princes Street, No. 70 in New Red desert sandstone stands out and is an early example (1886) of the use of this stone from Corsehill Quarry near Annan.

Across the foot of the Mound, in West Princes Street Gardens, the statue of the poet Allan Ramsay (1865) by Sir John Steell was carved out of Carrara marble and stands on a restored and cleaned yellowish sandstone base near the famous floral clock.

Princes Street—middle part

Before crossing to the north side of Princes Street pause to see how the original street of elegant sandstone town houses has been much altered by development and the ground floors submerged by later shop frontages. In 1954, at a time when it was expected that Princes Street might be rebuilt from end to end, a panel was set up to regulate New Town developments. The two massive shop and office blocks directly opposite, following the panel's recommendations, were built to include a first floor balcony, expected to set a pattern for later developments. The eastern block above the balcony is faced with alternating whitish travertine slabs and narrow grey granite slabs, the western block with large bluish-grey slabs. The travertine is probably Italian and the xenolithic granite is from the ancient Rubislaw Quarry just outside Aberdeen. At street level the shops are faced with assorted grey granites. Larvikite, a variety of syenite from Norway, has been used for the facing on Mothercare. The polished limestone conglomerate used to face Radio Rentals is of a variety known as Perlato Appia imported from Italy.

Thin slabs of fine-grained riven slate have been used on Elena Mae and the adjoining building to the east. Another cream Perlato conglomerate can be seen on Roland Cartier, this time a Sicilian stone. Springwell Quarry near Gateshead provided the sandstone on this shop.

Littlewood's store is faced above with sandstone quarried in the Millstone Grit at Heworthburn near Felling on the south bank of the River Tyne. This sandstone sometimes had a bluish-grey colour when fresh but here the colour has been lost. Stonework around the entrance is enlivened by harder rocks: a polished grey medium-grained granite above the doors which could be from Rubislaw Quarry, an unpolished grey gneiss behind the shop name and a polished brown coarse-grained syenitic rock at either side of the doors.

The original house fronts in droved sandstone with polished quoins can be seen in some buildings before Frederick Street. At the corner Salisbury's is faced with creamy bioclastic limestone and greyish blue larvikite.

Frederick Street

At street level new shop fronts obscure the original sandstone frontages up Frederick Street, although the original sandstone can be seen in higher floors, some recently cleaned. A great variety of facing stones have been used. Fastframe, Martin's Light Bite Restaurant and John Smith's Wools share a facing of cream-coloured limestone full of crinoid, bivalve and bryozoan fragments. The facing on Millet's is a brecciated serpentine marble, with dark reddish fragments in a pale green matrix very similar to the marble known as Rosso Antico d'Italia, which comes from Genoa. The next shop has a very light grey granite facing from Baveno in the Piedmont district of North-west Italy. The Stakis Steak House and the Anglia Building Society have a very dark green larvikite.

At the junction with George Street, the Woolwich Building Society has three varieties of facing granite: round some windows a very light medium-grained granite is very probably also from Baveno. There is also a grey coarse-grained granite and, in panels between windows, a dark greenish-grey medium-grained granite with aligned felspars and occasional xenoliths. Under the windows a highly polished black medium-grained stone of the type known as Black Bon Accord, comes from Sweden and is intermediate in composition between a diorite and a gabbro.

Across George Street the Nationwide Building Society on the corner opposite has a delicate shade of pink granite facing very similar to another of the Baveno granites. It is accompanied by a dark pink variety which is very like Scottish Corrennie from near Alford, Aberdeenshire.

The bronze statue of William Pitt at the junction of George Street and Frederick Street stands on a grey sandstone plinth.

George Street—from Frederick Street to Hanover Street

On the south side of George Street, No. 68–70, the Sun Alliance Office (1955), is mostly faced with polished Blaxter stone, a buff micaceous, yet featureless sandstone, from Elsdon, Tyne and Wear. Around the ground floor windows and along the base Black Bon Accord has been used again. The entrance steps are of green slate, probably Cumbrian.

No. 62–66, Bank of Scotland, originally the Union Bank, is built of polished Dalmeny stone, a greyish sandstone from West Lothian. This stone has weathered well apart from the balustrade and one column at the eastern entrance where cement repairs have been necessary.

The Assembly Rooms, built in 1782 and 1817, are probably built of Craigleith stone. Later arches (1906–7) bridging lanes at each side are probably in a north English sandstone.

No. 39 across the street, Justerini and Brooks, is notable for the green Cumbrian slate facing.

No. 46 has been extensively restored with a modern droved finish, in Stainton brown sandstone from Durham above the rock-faced ashlar basement, and can be compared with the early 19th century dressing of the local sandstone in adjacent buildings.

No. 34, Reader's Digest, has a facing of highly polished grey dioritic rock, weathering badly.

No. 32, James Allan, and No. 30, P & O Travel, share facings of travertine. The Hanover Street front of P & O Travel is faced with a faded dark green serpentine marble, which could be Verde Imperiale from Genoa.

The statue of George IV at the junction stands on a plinth of grey porphyritic granite.

George Street—from Hanover Street to St. Andrew Square

The Commercial Union Insurance Building, originally the Edinburgh Life Assurance Co. Offices (1908–9), is the only building in Edinburgh constructed of Portland Stone, an Upper Jurassic white limestone from Dorset, though this stone is used elsewhere as facing. Harder shell fragments, including large bivalves, weather out on the surfaces. At the base is an unpolished grey granite.

The George Hotel is made out of three buildings: The Adam Rooms in grey polished ashlar with cement skinning above, The Chambertin Restaurant in freshly cleaned rusticated yellowish sandstone at street level and grey droved sandstone above is followed to the east by a grey polished sandstone building.

St. Andrew's Church (1785—one of the earliest buildings in George Street) has columns, buildings and steps of Craigleith stone, while the ashlar of Hailes Sandstone from Redhall Quarry is polished in front and droved behind. This uncleaned building shows little weathering. In the sandstone, laminar bedding and current-bedding can be seen near the entrance on the right.

The Royal Bank of Scotland, originally the head office of the Commercial Bank (1847), directly opposite, is in the form of a Graeco-Roman temple, built of Binny Sandstone, mostly polished, each large Corinthian-style column made up of ten stones.

The Life Association of Scotland, adjoining, has an alternation of polished and flame textured grey granite. The bulk of the building is faced with Rubislaw granite from Aberdeen on the main facades and gables. On recessed areas round windows on ground floor level and in the entrance black Bon Accord has been used. Grey Creetown granite from Kirkcudbright forms the copings, sills and mullions. Just inside the entrance Imperial Grey marble from France can be seen and on the main staircase and just visible another French marble, Bois Jordan, which is grey with pink and white patches.

St. Andrew Square—west side

The westernmost part of the Guardian Royal Exchange building (1940) has buff sandstone above its gabbro-faced lower storey. The origin of the sandstone was Heworthburn Quarries in the Millstone Grit from Felling, Durham. The eastern part of the same Guardian Royal Exchange building at the end of George Street continues the black Bon Accord at ground floor level with Creetown light grey granite above.

The Scottish Widows' Fund & Life Assurance and Manpower Service's building (1962) next door, is once again faced with black Bon Accord which continues inside the building in the entrance hall where it is used together with Carrara marble. The upper part of the outside of this building is clad in Derbydene Carboniferous limestone, a grey fossiliferous stone from Matlock in Derbyshire. Large bivalve shells can be seen even from street level.

The Standard Life Assurance building (1901) has a large frontage on the corner with the north side of George Street, built of a pale yellow sandstone, polished at ground level, rusticated up to the first cornice and polished above that. The stone is likely to have come from Northumberland and the newer part of the building fronting the square has a sandstone facing, perhaps from Blaxter.

In the centre of the square the monument to Henry Dundas, Viscount Melville was completed in 1821 in Cullalo sandstone, with the statue added in 1828.

St. Andrew Square—north side

The first six houses are original, built between 1770 and 1775, though much altered. No. 21 has a droved ashlar west gable with the basement partly coursed rubble, and a front refaced in polished ashlar with an added Doric porch. No. 22 has coursed rubble below, coarsed, squared rubble above and an added Corinthian porch. No. 23 is in greyer polished sandstone with an Ionic porch. No. 24 has yellow sandstone and a Doric porth. No. 25 has a porch in Blaxter-type sandstone, added in 1964. The walls are stuccoed as they would have been when the house was first built. No. 26 shows the original random rubble.

The Scottish Equitable building (1899) replaced the other houses in this row, using characteristic purplish grey Doddington sandstone.

Queen Street

The National Portrait Gallery (1890), reached down North St. Andrew Street, was the first large building in Edinburgh to use New Red Sandstone, quarried from Moat near Carlisle and Corsehill at Annan. The main walls are in regular, coursed, rock-faced rubble, while the flanking buttresses, window dressings and doors are of polished ashlar in which dune-bedding can be seen. The paired windows on the first floor level have grey coarse-grained granite pillars in the arches. The red sandstone has suffered from erosion and has been necessary to remove the corner spirelets. The restoration, due to be completed by 1991, includes rebuilding the spirelets using red sandstone saved from a former Caledonian Railway viaduct in Leith and from the specially reopened Corsehill Quarry.

St. Andrew Square—east side

The large office block over the Eastern Scottish Bus Station (1970) is faced with Prudham stone, a buff, coarse-grained, slightly micaceous sandstone.

No. 35 and No. 36 were built as a pavilion for Dundas House from a polished light micaceous sandstone, full of black silty streaks or feaks.

Dundas House (1774), now head office of the Royal Bank of Scotland, was built of Hailes Sandstone from Redhall Quarry as a private house for Sir Laurence Dundas. A feature of this house is the remarkable domed ceiling over the main concourse of the bank. Outside, on the right of the building, weathering has picked out cross-lamination in the sandstone.

The Bank of Scotland building to the south, completed in 1852 for the British Linen Bank, is an elaborate structure in Binny Sandstone, rusticated up to balcony level.

The Royal Bank of Scotland next to it was originally the head office of the National Bank of Scotland (1936) and is faced up to the first floor level with a rusticated yellowish sandstone from Darney in the north of England. Along the base is a grey granite from Rubislaw, Aberdeen, containing felspar laths and large black xenoliths.

St. Andrew Square—south side

One of the most striking of the modern buildings in the square is the Scottish Provident Institution building (1961), which makes impressive use of a grey Italian gneiss, likely to have come from Novara.

On the south-east corner of the square the former Prudential Office (1895) is faced with New Red Sandstone from Dumfriesshire while the lower part, up to the springers of the window arches uses Peterhead granite.

South St. Andrew Street

Notable among stones seen here is Rankin's in blue larvikite. The Job Centre and adjacent building to the north are faced with a yellow Carboniferous sandstone, from Wellfield near Huddersfield. No. 7–9 (1883) is in coarse Cragg sandstone from Northumberland.

Princes Street—south side

From the foot of South St. Andrew Street is an impressive view of the 60 m high Scott Monument (1846) built of Binny Sandstone and extensively restored in the 1970's using Permian sandstone from Clashach Quarry, Hopeman in Moray and a very little Blaxter stone. It stands tribute to the famous author, Sir Walter Scott, whose statue has been carved of Carrara marble by Sir John Steell.

Also on the south side of Princes Street is the newly completed Waverley Market in pale grey flame-textured Portuguese granite, with large white felspars. This stone already shows signs of oxidation on the west side exposed to the weather.

Princes Street—east end

The Royal British Hotel (1898) is faced with badly weathered sandstone and has Peterhead granite columns on its windows. Both the hotel and Dorothy Perkins' shop have facings of light grey granite with large white felspars and xenoliths.

The former Woolworth's building (1925) is faced with buff sandstone which may be from Prudham. Some minor alterations at a later date used Blaxter sandstone. This building has now been divided into several shops. Those so far opened are mostly faced with a cream coloured bioclastic sandstone, though one has polished green volcanic tuff facing.

Robert Adam's Register House was begun in 1774. After careful examination of local building stones, Adam chose Craigleith Sandstone and Hailes Sandstone. Interruptions owing to cash shortage and the Napoleonic War delayed completion until 1834 by which time Binny Sandstone was in vogue. Cleaning in 1969 has revealed the yellowish appearance of the latter stone. The ashlar is rusticated to first floor level and polished above. Extensions in 1882 used sandstone from Longannet in Fife. The bronze statue of the Duke of Wellington by Steell rears up on a plinth of Peterhead granite.

Across the street, the North British Railway Hotel was completed in 1902 in cream Prudham sandstone, a stone seen to better advantage in the distance in the recently cleaned Scotsman Building (1902) at the south end of the North Bridge.

The Renaissance style Post Office (1866) was originally built of Binny Sandstone, but has been enlarged twice. In 1890 the back, to the south, was doubled in the same stone, but purplish Doddington stone was used for an extension to the south-west and for another floor completed in 1909.

Waterloo Place—Regent Road

Almost all the stone for Waterloo Place (1822) came from Hailes Quarry, but many buildings have since been refaced with another sandstone. Waterloo Place connects Princes Street with Calton Hill across the ice-gouged Low Calton ravine by means of the Regent Bridge (1819), a Napoleonic War Memorial constructed in Craigmillar stone.

The Governor's House is the only part of the old Calton Gaol still standing. It was built of Hermand sandstone from the Upper Oil Shale Group in West Lothian. St. Andrew's House, on the site of the rest of the Calton Gaol, was completed just before the Second World War, by which time little stone was quarried in Edinburgh. It was cheaper to transport polished sandstone from Darney as facing panels for this steel-framed building. Darney blends with other Edinburgh monuments and buildings and is resistant to grime. Fine light grey Creetown granite was chosen from the walls along Regent Road and for the mullions of the main staircase windows. Black Bon Accord granite was used for decorative work at other entrances and windows.

Calton Hill

The former Royal High School building, begun in 1825 as a replacement for the original school in High School Yards in the Old Town, and more recently adapted for use of the proposed Scottish Assembly, is built of Craigleith Sandstone. Many other buildings on the Calton Hill are built of the same stone, including Observatory House (1792), the Nelson Monument (1816), the City Observatory (1818) and Playfair's Monument (1827). Most impressive of all is the incomplete National Monument to the Scottish Dead of the Napoleonic War. Started in 1823, work was abandoned in 1829, though several later plans were put forward for its completion. Part of a particularly large stone, dug out of Craigleith Quarry soon after work on the monument began, went to the architrave; the rest of this stone went to Buckingham Palace. The twelve pillars are made of the commoner of the two types of freestone from Craigleith laid on its natural bed. The Dugald Stewart Monument (1831) is built of light yellow Humbie freestone from West Lothian, also used for the Burns Monument (1830) across Regent Road. Extensive refacing of the latter monument in 1978 has meant that it is now almost all Darney stone that is seen there.

The summit of the Calton Hill marks the end of the walk. It is a fine vantage point from which to survey the local geology. Prominent to the south east is the Salisbury Crags teschenite sill and the vents and lava flows of the Arthur's Seat volcano, of which Calton Hill is a faulted fragment (Arthur's Seat Excursion). Ice erosion moulded these crags into their present form, just as it sculpted the crag and tail which forms the head and backbone of the Old Town (Castle Hill Excursion), where this walk started.

I. Bunyan

BLACKFORD HILL AND DREGHORN

O.S. 1:50000 Sheet 66 Edinburgh
B.G.S. 1:50000 Sheet 32E Edinburgh
B.G.S. 1:25000 Edinburgh Special Sheet
Route: Map 6

BLACKFORD HILL is the northern continuation of the Lower Devonian Pentland Hills Volcanic Rocks (Mykura 1960, 1962). The hill is formed of basic andesite and trachyte lava flows. Low ground round the north and west of the hill is underlain by red sandstones of the Upper Old Red Sandstone. Blackford Hill was moulded into its present crag-and-tail shape by an easterly-flowing ice-sheet. The ice laid bare the rocky crags round the west side of the hill, and, deflected to either side of the hill, gouged deep hollows now occupied on the north side by Blackford Pond and on the south side by the alluvium of the Braid Burn. The gently sloping tail on the eastern (leeward) side of the hill is followed by Observatory Road.

The excursion is concerned with both volcanic rocks and glacial features and also looks at several buildings of geological and other interest. Two hours should be sufficient time for the excursion, but extra time should be added for visits to the public buildings and for Dreghorn (Locality 14). Lothian Region Transport bus routes pass along the roads north and east of Blackford Hill. Parking is available on these roads and also opposite the Observatory.

1. Grant Institute of Geology

For over 200 years Edinburgh University has been renowned as a centre for geological research. This tradition continues in the Grant Institute of Geology, named after its benefactor, Sir Alexander Grant. The masonry of the main building, dated 1931, is grey Carboniferous sandstone from Blaxter Quarry, Northumberland. The more modern extension on the east side houses high temperature and pressure experimental petrology laboratories.

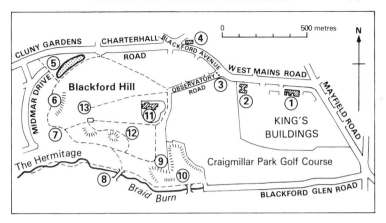

MAP 6. Blackford Hill

2. Murchison House: British Geological Survey

This modern yellow brick building houses the Scottish office of the Survey, founded in 1835. Its name derives from Sir Roderick Murchison, Director of the Survey when mapping started in Scotland in 1854. Survey research includes land and offshore geology, geophysics, seismology and geomagnetism. Murchison House has the largest public geological reference library in Scotland with over 30000 books, 150000 serial volumes and 15000 maps. The bookstall stocks geological maps, books and other products for sale to the public. Murchison House is open during weekdays only.

FIG 11. Harrison Arch

3. Harrison Arch

Commanding the entrance to Observatory Road, this fine arch of Permian red sandstone from Dumfries, has inscriptions commemorating George Harrison and the sale of Blackford Hill to the City of Edinburgh in 1884 (Figure 11).

4. Reid Memorial Church

The Gothic-style church was designed by Leslie Graham Thomson in 1933. Pink Upper Old Red sandstone from Hawkhill Wood Quarry, Craigmillar, was used to build the church and Doddington Stone, a Carboniferous sandstone from Wooler, was imported for the facing stone.

5. Blackford Pond: Ice Gouge, Erratics

The pond lies in a hollow gouged out by ice deflected round the north side of Blackford Hill. The work of ice can also be seen in two dolerite erratics, transported from one of the sills to the west, and now embedded in granite setts near the Midmar Drive entrance (Figure 12).

FIG 12. Dolerite erratics

6. Quarry: Andesite Lavas

Above the path up from the pond is an overgrown quarry cut out of the western face of Blackford Hill. The lowest rock seen is a pale trachytic lava overlain by a thin agglomerate containing trachyte blocks. Above this the main quarry face was cut into the single flow of dark fine-grained basic andesite which forms most of Blackford Hill.

7. Boundary Wall: Sandstone, Andesite

Note how the availability of stone is reflected in the wall along the path. Opposite the quarry dressed pink and white sandstones make up the entire wall. Further south angular purple andesite blocks and the occasional rounded erratic were used in constructing the wall but softer dressed sandstone blocks were preferred for embedding the posts.

8. Braid Burn: Ice Gouge, Glacial Channel

On coming round the hill the valley now occupied by the Braid Burn opens out to view. The burn is a misfit in such a large valley. Originally the valley was carved out by ice deflected round the south side of Blackford Hill, but was then further deepened as the ice melted and spilled torrents of water from the Water of Leith at Colinton through the Hermitage of Braid. The steep northerly side of the valley is cut in andesite lava while on the gentler southern slopes the andesite lava is mantled by boulder clay.

9. Blackford Hill Quarries: Andesite Lava

Extensive quarrying for road-metal on the southern slopes of Blackford Hill has produced several faces exposing andesite lava, much of it badly altered. Weathering to red or purple, the fresh andesite is dark grey and finely-crystalline with sparse phenocrysts of plagioclase, augite and biotite, set in a matrix showing flow-texture. Veins of red jasper and green chlorite cut the rock. The newer quarry to the east is being infilled with refuse.

10. Agassiz Rock: ?Glacial Striae

Set near the bottom of the valley, this rock has been protected as a site of Special Scientific Interest, as one of the localities where in 1840 the Swiss geologist Louis Agassiz identified the erosive action of ice in Scotland. Designation, however, has not protected the rock from natural erosion. Frost-shattering has caused part of the rock to fall and all but destroyed the horizontal scratches Agassiz identified as striae along its base. Although other interpretations, such as erosion by glacial meltwater and slickensiding, have been put on these scratches, this site still remains a landmark in the understanding of Scottish glacial geology.

11. Corbie Craig: Crag-and-tail

Return east by the Braid Burn and up the path from the bridge. South-east of the summit Corbie Craig forms a superb example of the glacial crag-and-tail feature. It demonstrates in miniature the form of Blackford Hill itself.

12. Blackford Hill: Views from the Summit

A climb to the summit of Blackford Hill is rewarded on a clear day with panoramic views of central Scotland. All the nearby hills are formed of Carboniferous or Devonian igneous rocks, the intervening low ground being generally drift-covered sedimentary rocks. Dominating the view to the north-east are the remains of the Arthur's Seat volcano, with the cliffs of the Salisbury Crags teschenite sill and the columnar basalt of Samson's Ribs. Edinburgh Castle to the north sits on a dolerite plug and forms a fine crag-and-tail feature with the Royal Mile. The hills of Fife across the Firth of Forth, and of East Lothian, are mainly Lower Carboniferous lavas and intrusions, and the hills to the west are mainly teschenite or quartz-dolerite sills.

Older, Devonian, volcanic rocks form the Pentland Hills running south-west from Blackford Hill and also the Ochil Hills across the River Forth to the north-west. In the west, flat-topped bings of spent shale from the once-thriving West Lothian oil-shale industry contrast with a more distant conical coal bing in the Central coalfield. To the south-east rounded Southern Upland hills are made of Lower Palaeozoic grey-wackes and shales. Together with southern Highlands hills of metamorphic Dalradian rocks, seen far to the north-west, they enable the full width of the Midland Valley to be appreciated.

13. The Royal Observatory, Edinburgh: Visitor Centre

Dominating the east slopes of Blackford Hill is the Royal Observatory, its stone building constructed of grey sandstone from Doddington and Hailes quarries. Originally moved here from Calton Hill in 1896 to escape the city lights, the observatory now has telescopes as far afield as Australia and Hawaii. The wide range of astronomical research can be viewed in the Visitor Centre, which is open on weekdays and on afternoons at weekends.

14. Dreghorn Spur: Upper Old Red Sandstone Sediments

A fine, easily accessible section in the Upper Old Red Sandstone sediments which overlie the Lower Devonian volcanic rocks of Blackford Hill, has been cut for the Dreghorn Spur (NT 231 684) of the Edinburgh City Bypass. From Blackford Hill drive west along Cluny Gardens to Morningside, south along the A702 for 3 km to the Bypass, west along the Bypass for 1·5 km, and take the Dreghorn Spur north to Redford Road where parking is permitted. Access to the west side of the cutting is along the footpath. Do not cross over this busy road.

The cutting is capped by 1 to 2 m of grassed till on an undulating rockhead, which has been gouged deeply at the west end of the footbridge. The section on the west side of the cutting exposes almost 50 m of Upper Old Red Sandstone sediments, dipping at 15° to 25° to the south-west and cut by several small faults. Sandstone is the dominant lithology, in beds up to 5 m thick, ranging in colour through pale purple, dark purple, pink and white. Some beds of sandstone are fine-grained, other beds are medium to coarse-grained with pebbly bands containing mudstone flakes as well as quartz and cornstone pebbles. The sandstones vary from poorly bedded to well-bedded, in places cross-bedded. Thin beds of grey-green, red-purple or brick red mudstones and siltstones lie between the sandstones. Cornstone nodules can be found in one of the finer bands near the south end of the section. Cornstones are concretionary limestones similar to calcretes, indicative of the semi-arid climate of Upper Old Red Sandstone times. A NW-dipping fault with a small throw is well exposed 150 m south of the footbridge.

The two sides of the cutting provide interesting insight into the contrasting engineering problems produced by dipping bedded rocks. On the east side where the beds dip towards the road it has been necessary to strip off whole layers along bedding planes; in addition holes have been drilled to drain water from the sandstones. A much steeper face has been left on the west side where the beds dip into the bank. Here the sandstone blocks are more stable but softer mudstone and siltstone beds have been walled over to prevent erosion.

A. D. McADAM

GRANTON AND WARDIE SHORE

O.S. 1:50 000 Sheet 66 Edinburgh
B.G.S. 1:50 000 Sheet 32E Edinburgh
Route: Map 7

THE sediments exposed along the shore between Silverknowes and Newhaven belong to the Lower Oil-Shale Group (Holkerian-Asbian) of the Lower Carboniferous Calciferous Sandstone Measures. These beds rest upon the Arthur's Seat Volcanic Rocks (Table 2). They are largely non-marine and were apparently deposited in a large freshwater or brackish lake extending into West Lothian and Fife and as far as the Pentland Hills. This lake, however, was subject to a periodic marine influence from the east, which became more manifest through time. Marine fossils in the Edinburgh district are confined to thin bands only. Non-marine or marginal marine fossils, however, are common at certain horizons, especially bivalves, ostracods, crustaceans, and fishes.

In northern Edinburgh the Lower Oil-Shale Group is folded into a dome with the underlying Abbeyhill Shales in the core of the dome at Drylaw. The WSW-ENE trending Granton Fault, which outcrops 800 m west of Granton Harbour, displaces the strata but good sections of the Granton Sandstones and the overlying Wardie Shales are to be found respectively to the west and east of the harbour (Tait, 1925).

Excursion A—Granton shore

This excursion can only be undertaken at low tide; total time 2 hours.

1. Craigleith Sandstone

From West Shore Road, just west of the Granton Gasworks (NT 220 773) follow the esplanade below Craigroyston House and Muirhouse. The sports ground was reclaimed from

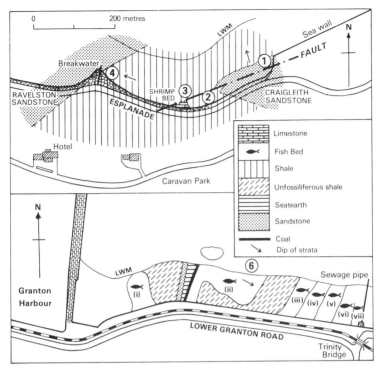

MAP 7. Granton and Wardie shore

the site of the Old Granton Land and Sea Quarries, formerly quarried for building stone. From the western corner of the high sea wall observe the Craigleith Sandstone exposed in the high ground to the south, across the wave-cut platform forming the level public park. The top of this same sandstone is exposed on the shore below the esplanade. The sandstone is yellowish, current-bedded and coarse to fine grained.

2. Bituminous Shale

Directly overlying the Craigleith Sandstone is a bituminous shale bearing large ironstone nodules, sometimes containing poorly preserved fish remains. The shale, where exposed, contains abundant conchostracans. This forms a wave-cut platform upon which rests the Granton Shrimp Bed.

3. The Granton Shrimp Bed

The sequence overlying the bituminous shales contains three thin dark blue-grey calcareous horizons separated by shales (Briggs and Clarkson, 1983). Each horizon consists of thin organic laminae alternating with dolomite. The uppermost horizon, up to 30 cm thick, rests directly on a shale which in places is highly disturbed with NW-trending parallel folds normal to direction of slumping. The troughs of some 10 cm amplitude are filled with contorted material of the shrimp bed. Above this is a brecciated horizon, containing fragments of marine fossils, succeeded by finely laminated calcareous shrimp-limestone once more.

The upper calcareous bed contains abundant specimens of crustaceans; common *Waterstonella grantonensis*, rarer *Crangopsis*, and *Anthracophausia*, and very rare *Tealliocaris*. There are also hydroids which like the crustaceans, are preserved in fluorapatite. Palaeoniscid fishes are sometimes found, and several specimens of a conodont-bearing animal have been recorded. These fossils are found only in isolated patches a few metres across and the locality is now largely worked out, the bulk of the fossiliferous material having been removed to the Royal Museum of Scotland in 1985.

The site is now protected as an S.S.S.I. under the vigilance of the Park Patrol. *It is illegal to hammer these exposures.* Shrimp-bearing blocks may however be picked up amongst the pebbles on the beach.

4. Western Breakwater

Follow the esplanade as far as the point or walk along the pebble and sand beach. Sandy ribs with shaly partings dipping 12° WNW mark the base of the yellow Ravelston Sandstone. The thin shales within the sequence are in places crowded with ostracods. Exposures further along are very poor.

Return to West Shore Road via the esplanade.

5. West Side Granton Harbour: Wardie Shales and Coal (not shown on map)

From Granton Harbour walk westwards along the shore (241 770). The sequence is not well exposed but some 100 m from the western breakwater is an outcrop of the Wardie

Coal. It is less than a metre thick but was formerly extracted. Just above the coal is a thin (20 cm) band of pyritous limestones and shales with *Lingula*, bivalves, and ostracods followed by black shales with ironstone nodules. The succession is intruded by thin olivine-dolerite sills. The General's Rock, 300 m west of the breakwater, shows the top of the Ravelston Sandstone.

Apart from the Wardie Coal, however, the sequence is better seen east of Granton Harbour.

Excursion B—Shore East of Granton Harbour

6. Wardie Shales

This excursion can only be undertaken at low tide: total time 1½ hrs.

This section in the Wardie Shales was the source of many of the fishes described in the early nineteenth century by Agassiz, and later by Traquair (1887–1914), who published an extensive faunal list in 1903. The sequence was detailed by Mitchell *et al.* (1962) and later by Wood (1975) who collected many fossil fishes from a particular horizon.

Much of the succession is of shale with ironstone nodules but there are some thin ostracod-bearing limestones. Some of the nodules bear fish remains but the vast majority contain only coprolites usually of spiral form. This stretch of shore is rather contaminated and it is recommended that any nodules should be boiled before breaking open to remove effluent.

The succession dips eastwards at about 10°. The sequence, as given by Mitchell *et al.* and amended by Wood (1975), is as follows:

		metres
	Fish Bed (vii)	7·6
Black shales with ironstone	Fish Bed (vi)	5·0
nodules containing fish remains	Fish Bed (v)	4·7
	Fish Bed (iv)	2·0
	Fish Bed (iii)	0·9
Coprolitic bituminous shale		7·6
(beds not exposed)		
Black shales with thin limestone,		
Lingula and bivalves (beds largely	Fish Bed (ii)	3·0
unexposed but thin tuff bed 2·5 cm visible)		
Wardie Coal (not now exposed)		1·0

Nodular seatearth		1·4
Yellow sandstone		3·5
Unfossiliferous argillaceous beds with nodules; grey papery shale		6·4
Dark papery shale	Fish Bed (i)	2·1

The lower part of the succession below the Wardie Coal is sparsely fossiliferous though some fishes have been collected from Fish Bed (i). Move eastwards over these thin papery shales (which have few nodules) as far as the 1·2 m thick cross-bedded sandstone unit standing up as a prominent ridge with an undulating top. Directly below this the trace-fossil *Thalassinoides* can be seen at the top of the underlying shale. The sandstone is overlain by a non-marine seatclay, above which lay the Wardie Coal, though this is no longer exposed.

Eastwards from the sandstone are the most productive fish-bearing beds (especially Beds v–vii), with many ironstone nodules. Different types of nodules can be referred to specific beds. Many such nodules lie in abundance amongst the pebbles though the vast majority contain only coprolites.

The fishes that have been recorded are:

Cosmoptychius striatus (Ag)
Nematoptychius greenocki (Ag)
Elonichthys robisoni (Hibb)
Elonichthys punctatus (Ag)
Gonatodus punctatus (Ag)
Eurynothus crenatus Ag
Rhadinichthys brevis Traq
Rhadinichthys carinatus (Ag)
Rhadinichthys ferox Traq

Rhadinichthys ornatissimus (Ag)
Wardichthys ornatissimus
Cladodont undet.
Ctenacanths undet.
Tristychius sp. nov.
Acanthodes sulcatus Ag
Rhizodus hibberti (Ag in Hibb)
Megalichthys sp.
"Ophiderpeton"

Those that are asterisked * are the most abundant.

East of the sewage pipe exposures are few and mud and the debris of new construction cover the beds.

Return to Granton Harbour.

E. N. K. Clarkson

GOSFORD BAY—ABERLADY POINT

O.S. 1:50000 Sheet 66 Edinburgh
B.G.S. 1:50000 Sheet 33W Haddington
Route: Map 8

THIS excursion is intended primarily to illustrate the cyclic pattern of the sedimentation of Carboniferous (Dinantian) rocks exposed between Craigielaw Point and Aberlady Point. Cyclic sedimentation is the term used to describe sequences of rocks where different types (representing differing environments of deposition) tend to occur over and over again in a certain order. Carboniferous rocks at Aberlady show a type of cycle which in upward sequence may be marine limestone, shale, sandstone, seatearth, coal, marine limestone . . . though occasionally units may be very thin or absent. There have been many theories put forward to explain cyclic sedimentation, but it must be emphasised that differences in scale and type make one single explanation unlikely. In the Aberlady area the cycles are considered to represent the normal sequence of events one would expect in a subsiding delta. Periodically, the trees growing on the muds and sands of the deltas died and were covered by the sea, in which limestone was formed, before the next influx of mud and sand shallowed the water sufficiently for another forest to establish itself. The seatearths in which traces of rootlets can be seen represent fossil soils.

The journey from Edinburgh may be made by Lowland Scottish service bus (North Berwick) or by car on the A198 road. Before reaching the main area of the excursion, however, the opportunity can be taken to examine a raised beach and a dolerite sill of Stephanian age at the southern end of Gosford Bay (localities 1 and 2, not shown on route-map). After leaving Longniddry and joining the Port Seton road at the coast stop at the Longniddry Bents parking place (NT 443 777) just past the road junction. Walking distance from locality 2 to the beginning of the main excursion at the

81

northern end of Gosford Bay (449 789) is about 1·25 km. The main excursion i.e. to localities 3 to 12 and thence to Aberlady, involves a walk of about 3·5 km. If the car is left at the northern end of Gosford Bay the walking distance to locality 12 and back is about 2·5 km. This half-day excursion should be carried out at low tide.

1. Gosford Bay (444 778): Raised Beach

The first locality is on the shore below bushes at the point where the broad sweep of Gosford Bay first comes into view. A small cliff about 4–5 m high shows a section of sandstone underlain by about 3 m of interbedded black micaceous carbonaceous shales (with plant fragments) and thin fine-grained sandstone bands with well developed ripple marks. On the beach below the cliff outcrops of some of the beds show excellent trace-fossils (e.g. worm casts and trails). The beds dip between 15°–20° towards the east and form part of the southern limb of the Gosford Bay Syncline. At the top of the cliff can be seen up to 2 m of raised-beach deposits containing at the base blocks of dolerite of presumed local origin, interstitial gravel and shells. Higher up shells and sand predominate. Oyster (*Ostrea edulis*) shells are most prominent along with *Patella*, *Littorina* and other species (Smith 1972, p. 40). The shelly horizon represents the intertidal portion of the main post-Glacial raised beach with the high water mark at the time of its formation being about 8 m O.D. This marine transgression of the Firth of Forth area, took place 5500 years ago.

2. Gosford Bay Sill, South (440 775)

At the seaward end of the small cliff baked shale is seen to be underlain by 'white trap'—the altered top of the Gosford Bay olivine-analcime-dolerite sill. (White trap is formed by the action, on the already crystallised rock-forming silicates, of CO_2 and other organic gases driven out of carbonaceous sediments by heat, and consists of the carbonates of lime, magnesium and iron with kaolinite and muscovite.) The contact can be traced a considerable distance seawards.

Prominent sheet-jointing in the dolerite dips in the same direction as the contact, but south-westwards the joint-surfaces dip in the opposite direction, presumably indicating

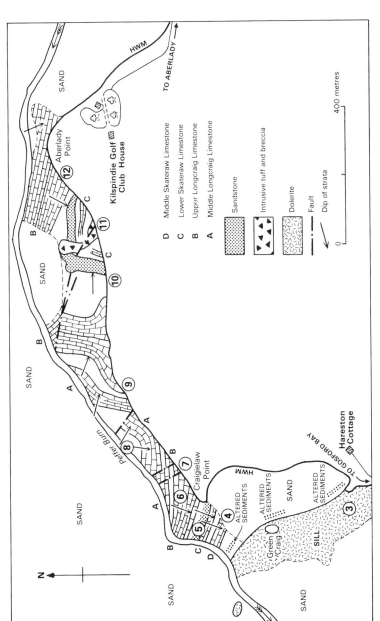

MAP 8. Kilspindie shore

Legend:

D — Middle Skateraw Limestone
C — Lower Skateraw Limestone
B — Upper Longcraig Limestone
A — Middle Longcraig Limestone

Sandstone

Intrusive tuff and breccia

Dolerite

— · — · — Fault

↘ Dip of strata

0 — 400 metres

Map labels: SAND, HWM, TO ABERLADY, Aberlady Point, Kilspindie Golf Club House, ⑫, ⑪, ⑩, ⑨, ⑧, ⑦, ⑥, ⑤, ④, ③, Petter Burn, Craigielaw Point, ALTERED SEDIMENTS, Green Craig, SILL, HWM, GOSFORD BAY, Hareston Cottage, TO GOSFORD BAY, N a change of attitude of the contact surface. The dolerite contains veinlets of calcite and quartz (in places amethystine) and patches of white trap are conspicuous. A large block of sandstone can be seen in the dolerite near the high water mark about 22 m from the contact. North-east of the contact, in Gosford Bay, outcrops are poor but sandstone and shale can be seen in places. For those particularly interested in volcanic phenomena a search at low tide may reveal the presence of two cryptovents (443 780 and 447 783) discovered by Howells (1969) but the continually shifting sand and shingle of Gosford Bay often covers them. Similar structures are more easily seen at locality 9. (See p. 119 for discussion on cryptovents).

3. Gosford Bay Sill, North

About 180 m past the North Lodge gates of Gosford House take the footpath northwards along the shore for about 800 m, noting the outcrops of dolerite on the shore. Just past the golf course green, west of Hareston Cottage, the base of the sill is reached. Here the dip of the sediments is towards the south-west as we are now on the north-eastern limb of the Gosford Bay Syncline. The contact is not visible but baked sandstone can be seen within a half-metre of it.

Outcrops of undulating beds of sandstone and shale appear through the sand a few metres north-east of the contact. Dolerite and white trap are also visible, probably indicating the presence of a thin offshoot below the main sill.

Walk northwards across the large expanse of sand to the north-west, keeping to the east of Green Craig where the contact of the sill and sediments can be located to within about a metre. The line of contact can be followed to the Peffer Burn, west of Craigielaw Point, and again an isolated outcrop to the east and below the main contact shows altered sediments.

4. Middle Skateraw Limestone (D)

About 45 m north-east, across the intervening sand, the dip slope of a well-jointed limestone (D) is visible. The surface is undulating slightly but in general the dip is about 15° to the south-south-west. The limestone is a hard massive dark-grey bed about 8 m in thickness. It contains crinoid fragments and productid brachiopods. Immediately below the overhanging limestone is a dark-grey mudstone which has been extensively bored by present-day molluscs.

5. Lower Skateraw Limestone (C)

The beds below limestone D are poorly exposed but at a distance of about 27 m the next limestone (C) is seen. This well-jointed limestone is about 1 metre in thickness and is a hard grey rock also containing crinoids and brachiopods. Careful search below the overhanging limestone shows about 2 cm of mudstone underlain by 3 to 5 cm of coal. This coal is followed downwards by a seatearth, sandy shale and sandstone and about 27 m north-east of the limestone a conspicuous false-bedded and ripple-marked sandstone crops out.

6. Upper Longcraig Limestone (B)

Below the false-bedded sandstone there is shale then flaggy limestone on top of pale-brown limestone with a nodular or 'rubbly' top surface. This lower part is dolomitic and contains many crinoid fragments. It forms a prominent scarp about 8·5 m high which continues seawards to form the Long Craig. There has been considerable undercutting of the soft shale and coal below this limestone. In places the coal reaches 25 cm in thickness and it is underlain by a seatearth.

7. Middle Longcraig Limestone (A) and Faults

Towards the east for a few metres there are many fallen blocks of limestone B before the lowest limestone (A) is seen. This is a particularly easy limestone to recognize; it is yellow-brown in colour and is made up largely of colonies of *Lithostrotion junceum* and *L. pauciradiale*. A field-name such as 'spaghetti-rock' or 'macaroni-rock' suggests itself immediately (cf. Catcraig, p. 134). The limestone is extremely fossiliferous containing, as well as compound corals, genera such as *Caninia* and *Zaphrentis*, and the brachiopods *Eomarginifera*, *Spirifer*, *Avonia*, *Pustula*, *Composita* and *Pugnoides*.

When traced towards high water mark (H.W.M.) the scarp of limestone B is seen to end abruptly and immediately below it can be seen limestone A. Higher up on the bank, just below the grass, the 'rubbly' limestone B can be seen again where it continues eastwards for about 18 m before it is thrown down again to beach level.

Two small north-westerly trending faults throwing up the strata between them cause this displacement of the outcrops. The effect can best be seen from the seaward end of the upthrown block.

8. Anticline in Middle Longcraig Limestone (A)

Limestone A can be followed eastwards along the shore, its dip decreasing until the crest of an anticline is reached. Below the limestone are sandstone and shales while in places thin (5 to 7 cm) sandstone dykes can be seen cutting the limestone. Excellent fossiliferous blocks can be found above H.W.M. below the golf course.

9. Middle and Upper Longcraig Limestones (B and C)

About 70 m east of the crest of the anticline the now easterly-dipping limestone is faulted and its base thrown up to near H.W.M. Keeping to H.W.M. limestone B can once again be identified because of its characteristic appearance. The bed can be followed along the shore to just below the octagonal blockhouse where it swings out to sea. The dip in this area is slight and the outcrop of the soft beds between limestones A and B has widened considerably.

The flaggy upper portion of Limestone B is also recognisable and above it, about 45 m east of the blockhouse at H.W.M. raised-beach deposits can be seen.

10. Sandstone and Shale

Continuing along H.W.M. a small cliff is reached exposing irregularly interbedded shale and sandstone. The shale forming a wave-cut platform at the base of this cliff contains productids and crinoids. Near the red-tiled cottage a false-bedded sandstone (cf. 5) is found at the top of the cliff. Farther east this sandstone can be seen swinging seawards and there is a small stack (the King's Kist) formed of an outlier of the sandstone which rests on undercut shales below.

11. Lower Skateraw Limestone (C) and Cryptovent

Eastwards from the red-tiled cottage the limestone C reappears and some 100 m from the cottage the axis of a syncline is reached. It has been breached by an elongate mass of volcanic breccia which can be seen (sometimes with difficulty because of shifting beach sand) to extend from H.W.M. for about 100 m seawards in a north-westerly direction. The breccia is made up of large fragments of limestone set in a matrix of broken-up shale, siltstone and tuffaceous material. Howells (1969) described this mass, and those mentioned previously in Gosford Bay, as cryptovents (small, roughly circular areas of highly disturbed strata, often with no trace of volcanic materials to confirm their volcanic origin). See discussion on p. 119.

12. Aberlady Point: Upper Longcraig Limestone (B)

West and east of Aberlady Point an extensive outcrop of limestone B is prominent, the dip being about 5° to the south.

From here the distance along the shore to Aberlady is about a kilometre. A footpath leads up to the church and from there it is 1·5 km back along the road to the starting point for locality 3. Alternatively the North Berwick–Edinburgh service bus passes through Aberlady.

P. McL. D. Duff

NORTH BERWICK

O.S. 1:50000 Sheets 66 Edinburgh and 67 Duns & Dunbar
B.G.S. 1:50000 Sheets 33W Haddington and 33E Dunbar
Route: Maps 9, 10, 11 and 12

THREE excursions are described to show typical examples of the volcanic and sedimentary rocks and some of the associated intrusions and volcanic vents so excellently exposed along 25 km of the North Berwick coast. The rocks are Dinantian (Calciferous Sandstone Measures) in age, and belong mainly to the volcanic facies known locally as the Garleton Hills Volcanic Rocks. The general succession is (McAdam and Tulloch, 1985):

Sediments, dolomitic, tuffaceous and cementstone facies
Trachytic tuffs and lavas—Bangley member
Basaltic lavas—Hailes member
Basaltic lavas—East Linton member
Basaltic tuffs, red ⎫
Cementstone bands ⎬ North Berwick member
Basaltic tuffs, green ⎭
Sediments, Canty Bay Sandstone, red cementstone facies

Gentle post-Carboniferous folding and faulting has given the beds a regional dip to the west.

The volcanic succesion is thinner than in the Garleton Hills to the south, though most of the lava types are represented at North Berwick. At a late stage in the volcanicity basaltic and basanitic sills and dykes and phonolitic volcanic plugs were intruded into these rocks. Another feature of the volcanicity is the number of tuff and agglomerate-filled volcanic vents. These were first identified as vents by Cuthbert Day, a local geologist and geochemist, who in a series of papers described the geology of the whole North Berwick coast section. The vents and their relationship were further discussed by Martin (1955) and more recently by Leys (1982). Descriptions of deep-originating granulite blocks have been given by Graham and Upton (1978).

1. Basaltic lavas underlain by red tuffs. Paddling Pool, North Berwick

Excursion A, which goes east from North Berwick, covers the lower part of the sequence in descending order from the basaltic lavas to the Canty Bay Sandstone and the red cementstone facies. Excursion B continues east to study the many agglomerate- and basalt-filled vents around Tantallon, Seacliff and St. Baldred's, intruded into the tuffs and underlying sediments. Excursion C, going west from Yellowcraig, near Dirleton, looks at the upper part of the sequence in ascending order, from the basaltic lavas up to the dolomitic sediments. Each excursion is around 8 km long, and takes about 5 hours. As many of the exposures are on the foreshore, it is best to start each excursion *about 3 hours before low tide.* Dirleton, North Berwick and Tantallon all lie on the A198 road and can easily be reached by car or Lowland Scottish service bus from Edinburgh. At North Berwick parking is available at the Harbour and at Rhodes Braes, though this area is very busy during holiday months. Cars and coaches may be parked at Tantallon Castle, but the gates are locked outwith opening hours. A public car park at Tyninghame takes only a few cars. Ample parking is available at the car park beside the Yellowcraig Caravan Site, reached by taking the sign-posted road off the A198 at the east end of the Dirleton by-pass. Booklets available at Yellowcraig describe the rich natural history of this area.

Excursion A—North Berwick to Canty Bay
(Route: Map 9)

1. North Berwick Harbour: Basaltic Lavas

The excursion starts from the Harbour near the centre of North Berwick (NT 554 856). Round the point on which are the ruins of the pre-reformation kirk of St. Andrew's with St. Ninian's Aisle, the four lowest lavas in the volcanic sequence are exposed, each lava being of a different type of basalt or trachybasalt. Forming the west wall of the Harbour and Swimming Pool area is the topmost of these lavas, an olivine-basalt of Markle type some 17 m thick. The dark grey or purple basalt has numerous large labradorite phenocrysts and small brown iddingsite pseudomorphs after olivine (in these lavas the olivines are rarely found fresh). Towards the point the basalt is scoriaceous with vesicles and large calcite amygdales. Below the Markle basalt is a flow about 10 m thick of pale purple-grey mugearite with sparse feldspar phenocrysts. The top of this flow is autobrecciated and scoriaceous with horizontally elongate vesicles. Calcite veins and prominant concentric iron-banding, produced by segregation of iron oxide into layers, have been picked out by differential weathering. Underlying the mugearite and forming the east wall of the harbour area is a 7 m flow of dark purple to grey Dunsapie basalt, resting on red bedded tuff. This has large phenocrysts of labradorite, augite and olivine, and also rare gabbroic xenoliths a few centimetres across.

Offshore Islands

Visible from North Berwick are several islands of igneous origin. Due north, the rounded Craigleith is an essexite laccolith, the joints in which indicate that erosion has uncovered the original shape of the intrusion. Famous as a home of the gannet, *Sula bassana*, and infamous historically as a prison, the Bass Rock, seen to the east, is a vertical volcanic plug of resistant phonolite. To the west, Fidra with its lighthouse and the Lamb are parts of a basalt sill. Excursion and charter boats sail to these islands from North Berwick, but *permission should be obtained before landing.*

2. Paddling Pool: Kulaite Lava, Red Tuffs, Cryptovent

Forming a low feature north from the west end of the Paddling Pool, and separated from the Dunsapie basalt by a few metres of red tuff, is the lowest lava in the volcanic sequence, a trachybasalt, a leucite-kulaite. It is a purple altered highly vesicular lava, some 4 m thick, with a reddened autobrecciated top. Altered hornblende and augite phenocrysts occur in a groundmass containing analcime, secondary after leucite (Bennett 1945). North-east of the Paddling Pool the rocky foreshore is formed of red bedded tuffs, agglomerates and marls with green reduction spots dipping at 15° to the north-west under the lavas. These beds accumulated in shallow lagoons during the early stages of volcanicity. At The Lecks the red tuffs are cut by a small cryptovent, a vent produced by volcanic gases (see p. 119). This can be picked out by the presence of steep dips and

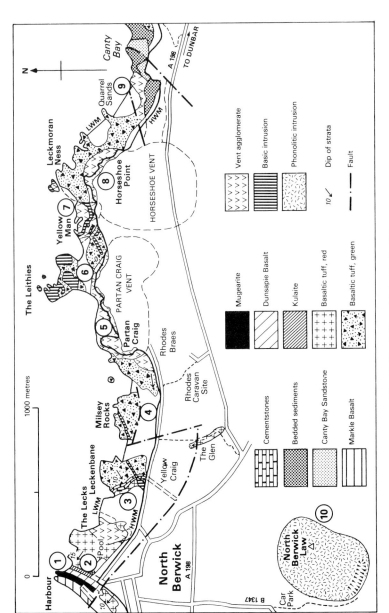

MAP 9. North Berwick to Canty Bay

large blocks of red tuff set in a matrix of red and green agglomeratic tuff. Small intrusions of dark analcime-basanite occur within the south-west margin of the vent. Beyond the vent there are further outcrops of undisturbed red bedded tuffs.

3. Leckenbane and Yellow Craig: Tuff Sequence and Intrusion

Crossing the intervening sand, make first towards the wave-cut platform of Leckenbane. Here a 3 m thick series of grey nodular cementstones with possible algal growths, and mudstones, separates the red tuffs and marls from green bedded tuffs below. Yellow Craig, a prominent rock near High Water Mark (H.W.M.), is a small oval plug of olivine-basalt intruded into the tuffs. The fresh centre of the intrusion is dark with small plagioclase and augite phenocrysts, whereas the chilled margin is pale and glassy. The intrusion continues to the north-east as thin basalt and agglomerate dykes. Three small cryptovents, one round the north of the intrusion, the other two cut by the dykes, contain disoriented blocks of red tuff, green tuff and cementstone.

4. Milsey Rocks: Green Tuffs, Sandstone

Across the sand towards Low Water Mark (L.W.M.) lies an area of fine green bedded tuffs. Prominent outliers of massive pale sandstone, terminated to the south by a fault, lie on the tuffs. A porphyritic basalt dyke, some 1·5 m wide, possibly a continuation of the Yellow Craig dykes, is displaced by several small faults and is split at its west end. Back across the sands towards H.W.M. green bedded tuffs are again exposed, their dip steepening as the Partan Craig Vent is approached. An area of disturbed blocks adjacent to this vent, possibly another cryptovent, has provided many granulitic blocks of deep-seated origin, taken as evidence of the rocks underlying the Midland Valley (Graham and Upton 1978).

5. Partan Craig Vent

This is one of the largest agglomerate-filled volcanic vents exposed along this coast. Seawards along its west margin the vent forms a feature, standing higher than the bedded tuffs lying outside the vent. The west-facing cliff of Partan Craig gives a fine section of the material filling the vent. A bedded reddish agglomeratic tuff near the base, containing large blocks of red-green bedded tuff and tuffaceous sandstone, represents a thick debris flow. Other agglomerates contain small blocks of red siltstone and pale cementstone, and bombs of nepheline-basanite, a lithology found locally only in intrusions. In the cliff the tuffs lie in a shallow collapse syncline, continued on the foreshore to the north as a prominent basin cut by intersecting thin calcite veins. Towards The Leithies low cliffs afford further sections through the vent agglomerate which has numerous angular blocks and bombs, and is cut by anastomosing calcite veins. The youngest rocks exposed in the north-east are tuffaceous sediments, probably deposited in a late-stage crater lake.

6. The Leithies: Basanite Sill

These small tidal islands, connected by a sand spit, are the dissected remains of an irregular basanite sill with columnar jointing. The sill has a veined amygdaloidal base, and the underlying green bedded agglomeratic tuff can be discovered in the intervening boulder-strewn ground. Remnants can be seen of the dolomitic agglomerate which formed the roof of the sill and in places altered the basanite to white trap. South of The Leithies the margin of the Partan Craig Vent can be traced near H.W.M. cutting coarse green bedded tuffs. A small north-east trending basin of cementstone lies on the tuffs. Just east of this an agglomerate and basanite dyke can be followed north-east acros the tuffs. The crag backed by a golf green on the post-Glacial raised beach is a small basanite plug.

7. The Yellow Man Vent

Beyond the basanite plug lies a small vent, notable for the large size, as much as 3 m across, of the red-green tuff blocks and basanite bombs embedded in its coarse green tuff matrix. These rocks are unbedded in the east, but form a basinal structure in the west where coarse layers may represent debris flows into a surface tuff ring. Two basanite dykes cutting the vent form upstanding stacks; the larger of these varies from 2 to 6 m wide, changes its direction across the vent, and splits into off-shoots. At its east margin the Yellow Man Vent cuts the earlier Horseshoe Vent.

8. Horseshoe Vent

Leckmoran Ness is a wave-cut platform formed of coarse green bedded tuffs with basanite bombs about 10 cm in diameter. The Ness is crossed by arcuate joints and intrusive brown tuffaceous sandstone dykes. The Horseshoe Vent agglomerates consist of poorly bedded green tuffs in a broadly basinal structure. The tuffs contain basanite bombs and blocks of sandstone, mudstone and bedded tuff, commonly 30 cm across, and are quite distinct from the finer grained tuffs outside the vent. The vent margin is excellently exposed along the shore towards Horseshoe Point, a locality where basanite bombs within the vent are particularly numerous.

9. Quarrel Sands and Canty Bay

Further outcrops of green bedded tuffs and tuffaceous sediments at the west of Quarrel Sands lie in a shallow syncline. Reddish-green agglomerates forming ridges in the middle of the sands belong to a small vent, whose south margin is seen abruptly truncating upstanding sandstones. These red and brown sandstones, with interbedded red silt-stones and mudstones and a porphyritic basalt dyke, are cut by a complex of small faults, one near H.W.M. striking east-west, the others striking north-west or north-east away from it. A landslip at the east end of the sands has carried massive blocks of sandstone on to the shore. Behind the landslip reddened cementstone facies sediments are seen overlying the Canty Bay Sandstone, a massive white, red and brown carious-weathering cross-bedded and contorted sandstone, which forms cliffs between the two bays and upstanding fault-bounded blocks on the foreshore. Red mudstones and siltstones crop out in the intervening low ground. On the foreshore east of Canty Bay red and green bedded tuffs are abruptly cut by the Gin Head Vent (Excursion B).

The excursion can be completed by returning along the clifftop path which starts at Horseshoe Point, or up the road at Canty Bay and via the A198 road and Rhodes Caravan Site or The Glen to North Berwick, observing the spectacular glacial crag-and-tail feature of the Law.

10. North Berwick Law: Phonolitic Trachyte Plug

The Law, a conical volcanic plug, forms an impressive crag and tail feature south of North Berwick. Access is gained from a car park to the west of the Law (553 843). A track leads south to the quarry which provided the stone that gives many North Berwick buildings their warm hue. This weathered red-mottled non-porphyritic medium-grained feldspathic rock is a phonolitic trachyte. The quarry has been partly infilled. Fresher rock can be obtained near the top of the Law. On a clear day the steep climb to the summit is further rewarded by a panoramic view of the Lothians, Fife and beyond. The main landmarks are pointed out by an indicator, and to the west, Arthur's Seat, the sleeping lion, bids one return to Edinburgh.

Excursion B—Tantallon to St. Baldred's
(Route: Maps 10 and 11)

1. Gin Head Vent: Basanite Intrusion, Vent Agglomerate

Parking for this excursion may be found at Tantallon Castle (594 848) which can be visited all year round (note closing time) or at Seacliff (607 845). The excursion starts at the west end of Canty Bay (587 852) reached by a track down from the A198 road. On the foreshore red and green bedded tuffs are cut abruptly by the upstanding west margin of the Gin Head Vent, which forms a prominent wave-cut platform. Green vent agglomerate is intruded by an irregular dissected sill of black, fine-grained, non-porphyritic, well-jointed basanite. The sill forms the stacks of Tapped Rock and Saddle Rock and the islet of Podlie Craig, while the green agglomerate occupies the lower shingle-covered ground. At H.W.M. below Taking Head, 100 m east of the last house, an irregular pale grey dyke cuts the darker roughly weathered basanite. The cliff on the west side of Gin Head consists entirely of green vent agglomerate with basanite bombs and large tuff blocks, while on the east side an inclined basanite sill is intruded into the agglomerate. The east margin of the vent cuts pink and white Canty Bay Sandstone which is traversed by W-E faults. Immense blocks of this sandstone are caught up in the vent both at Gin Head and in the cliffs 20 m north of a sewer pipe. This pipe goes along the northern margin of an older small vent filled with red bedded tuff and agglomerate, itself cut by the Gin Head Vent. In the cliffs above, the base of a basanite sill arches from vertical to horizontal and is picked out by a carbonate layer. Red ripple-bedded sandstones, mudstones and cementstone ribs crop out in the bay. *N.B. cliffs on the north of this bay make access difficult above half tide.*

2. Tantallon Vent: Vent Agglomerate

On the foreshore red bedded tuffs with large blocks and large basanite boulders, lying outside the vent, are exposed. The vent margin itself is obscured by shingle. Cliff sections show that the vent is filled with green unbedded tuff with small basanitic bombs. High up under the north wall of the castle is a large lenticular sandstone formed while the vent was dormant. Towards the middle of the vent there are zones with large reddish bedded tuff blocks and basanite bombs. The south part of the vent is mainly green bedded tuffs containing basanite bombs. Just beyond the waterfall amygdaloidal basanite bombs can be seen in white veined and impregnated agglomerate. Nearby there is a prominent curved basic dyke. The faulted southern margin of the vent can be seen in the cliff but is obscured by shingle where it crosses the foreshore.

3. Oxroad Bay: Green Bedded Tuffs

Cliffs on the south side of the bay comprise green bedded tuffs, with the low dip steepening towards the faulted vent margin. The green tuffs and fine agglomerate have planar and ripple-bedding, as well as contorted bedding possibly of algal origin. Yellow-weathering cementstone bands and ribs have yielded a diverse petrified flora of 23 species of pteridosperms and lycopods indicating a late Courceyan age (Barnard and Long 1975, Scott 1985). Networks of calcite and cementstone veins cut the tuffs. *N.B. The gully and cave beyond are impassable above half tide necessitating a walk round the cliff top.*

4. Seacliff Harbour, The Gegan: Red and Green Tuffs

Green bedded tuffs continue on the cliffs beyond the cave. However, a contact between green tuffs and red tuffs to the

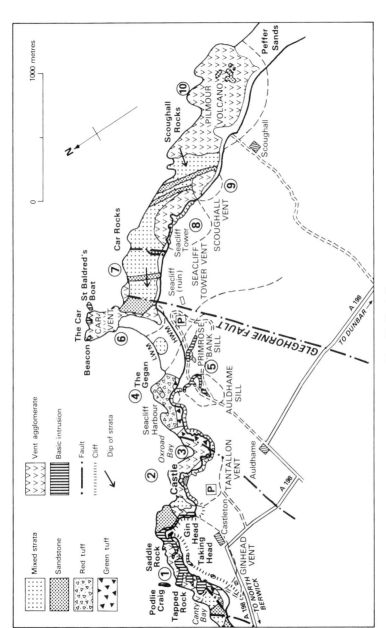

MAP 10. Tantallon

north can be followed on the foreshore. This junction continues vertically up the cliff beyond, where it cuts across the gently inclined bedding showing that the tuffs have been affected by secondary staining. Seacliff Harbour is cut into red bedded tuffs with large-scale cross-bedding. Fine agglomeratic bands in the tuff contain basic and intermediate bombs and blocks of marl and limestone. Prominent rectangular jointing and calcite veining in the tuffs have been picked out by the vegetation on the flat-topped stack of The Gegan. A small fault round the base of the cliff opposite is indicated by a sudded change of dip. The vertical contact between red and green tuffs is again visible on the cliff south of The Gegan and on the foreshore. The green tuffs have been stained red by oxidation of the ferrous iron, an effect possibly associated with the basic intrusions.

5. Auldhame Quarry, Primrose Bank: Basic Intrusions

Auldhame Quarry, now partly filled and overgrown, can be reached by climbing the grassy bank. The dark, fissile, well-jointed, fine-grained rock is a non-porphyritic basalt of Hillhouse type with celestite in veins. Whether the intrusion is a plug or sill is not clear. A contact with red bedded tuffs seen in the road cutting on the east side of the quarry is inclined at 45°, to the west. From here tuffs can be followed eastwards to where they overlie the Primrose Bank sill. The 15 m thick sill has an amygdaloidal top and is formed of dark purple Craiglockhart basalt, containing large black augite phenocrysts and small red-brown olivine pseudomorphs. The cave in the sill is related to a higher late-Glacial sea-level. From this part of the coast there are fine views of the phonolitic trachyte plug of the Bass Rock (Figure 13).

6. The Car Vent

Return to the shore by the car park on the post-Glacial raised beach. The Car rocks are part of a complex vent. At the south end a cryptovent is shown by disorientated blocks of red tuff and contorted sandstone. Red bedded tuff, with vesicular basalt bombs, fills the rest of the vent. This bedding has steep dips and is cut by numerous prominent joints. Small leucite-basanite intrusions occur at the beacon and

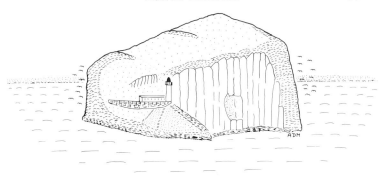

FIG 13. Bass Rock from Seacliff

St. Baldred's Boat. *N.B. Care should be taken to avoid being stranded by the tide.*

7. Car Rocks: Sediments, Gleghornie Fault

Just east of The Car Vent are thick white and red sandstones with ripple-bedding and contorted bedding. They are cut by numerous small SW-NE trending faults, part of the Gleghornie Fault. On the shore south-east of the fault gently NW-dipping reddened cementstone facies sediments consist of red and green mudstones, siltstones and fine sandstones with cementstone ribs. Two thick channel sandstones exhibit ripple-bedding, cross-bedding and contorted-bedding, the southerly sandstone being fault-bounded.

8. Seacliff Tower Vent

The eastern half of this vent is excellently exposed on the foreshore where red vent agglomerate forms an upstanding platform abruptly cutting the sediments. In the cliffs prominent gently inclined joint planes can be seen to lie at varying angles to the shallow to steeply dipping bedding. Below the ruined tower large tuff blocks are etched out by weathering and a few basic bombs occur. In the south blocks of sandstone, cementstone and other sedimentary rocks are caught up in the vent.

9. Scoughall Vent

The eastern half of this smaller red vent is also exposed on the shore. It is filled with red unbedded tuff and contains blocks of sandstone and bombs of red basalt. Joints in the vent dome away from the centre.

10. Pillmour Volcano

The poorly exposed Scoughall Rocks are mainly red bedded tuff, marl and sandstone filling a vent, notable for large sandstone blocks, up to 100 m across, at its south end.

The excursion can be completed by returning along the shore or by Scoughall to the A198. Alternatively continue south for 1·5 km across Peffer Sands and Ravensheugh Sands. Behind the intertidal sands high dunes of blown sand rest on the main post-Glacial raised beach which in turn covers a channel marking the pre-Glacial estuary of the River Tyne. The St. Baldred's area can also be reached from the car park at Tyninghame Links (627 809), and taking the track to ESE for 300 m to a bend, then the path through Links Wood to NNE to the noticeboard at H.W.M. The localities lie within the John Muir Country Park, permitted routes being indicated by 'green-footed' posts (Figure 14). The park commemorates John Muir, a native of Dunbar, revered in America as the person who had Yellowstone made the first of many National Parks in the United States.

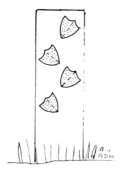

FIG 14. 'Duck's feet'

11. Ravensheugh, Frances Craig: Intrusions

At the south-east end of Ravensheugh Sands, about 200 m north-west of the forest path, is a prominent 15 m high cliff of dark columnar fine-grained teschenite, part of a sill which can be traced inland in outcrops and old quarries. At the base of the cliff, pale brecciated teschenite has been chilled against pink baked sandstone. Frances Craig, near L.W.M., is a complex faulted outcrop of brown sandstone and purple altered teschenite.

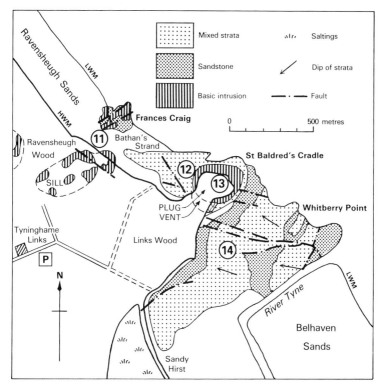

MAP 11. St Baldred's

12. Bathan's Strand: Sediments, Raised Beach

On the foreshore to the south-east, reddened bedded sediments dip gently and are cut by small faults. Fine-grained sandstones are interbedded with siltstones, mudstones and cementstone ribs. The same beds and the small faults are also exposed in the low cliffs on the peninsula to the south. Deposits of the post-Glacial raised beach on top of the sandstone cliff are very similar to deposits of the present beach. Angular basalt boulders lie in coarse shell sands with bleached whelks and limpets and purple mussels.

13. St. Baldred's Cradle: Basalt Plug

The peninsula is formed by a circular plug of Craiglockhart basalt (ankaramite) possibly a feeder for lavas in the Garleton Hills (p. 109). The junction between the plug and the sediments can be traced round the foot of the cliffs on three sides. Opposite the stone seat is St. Baldred's Cradle, the name given to a cleft excavated in the jointed rock. The fresh, dark fine-grained basalt has large black augite phenocrysts and small red-brown olivine pseudomorphs. An area of soft red vent agglomerate is exposed on the foreshore on the south-east side of the vent.

14. Whitberry Point: Sediments

Along H.W.M. a pale brown cross-bedded channel sandstone, dips gently WNW. Lower down the foreshore the underlying reddened bedded sandstones, siltstones and mudstones, are similar to those at Bathan's Strand. Small faults trending WNW-ESE cut these sediments, and to the south-west the channel sandstone has a faulted basal junction. The forest road leads north back to the car park.

Tyne Estuary (63 79): Sedimentation, Erosion

Active modern sedimentation and erosion, produced by river and tidal currents, can be seen around the Tyne estuary to the south. Sandy Hirst, a shingle and blown sand spit, is growing SSE from Tyninghame and the intertidal islet of Spike Island is growing north-west from West Barns. Curved spits along these show the direction of current action. Erosion is particularly marked on the south side of the estuary, producing good temporary sections in blown sand and beach sand, which can be reached from the south side of the Country Park at West Barns (651 787).

Excursion C—Yellow Craig to Cheese Bay
(Route: Map 12)

1. Yellow Craig: Vent Intrusion and Agglomerate

The excursion starts from the Yellowcraig car park (516 854). Take the path eastwards through the plantation and climb the small hill of Yellow Craig which forms a *roche moutonnée*. The Craig is a plug, lying within the Yellow Craig Vent, consisting of hard, black microporphyritic olivine-basalt. Surrounding Yellow Craig the extensive flat at about 8 m O.D. is a post-Glacial raised beach, covered in places by dunes of blown sand. East across a wall are several low outcrops of the vent agglomerate, a brown-grey tuff full of rounded bombs and baked angular blocks. Careful study will show they include Markle basalt, mugearite, bedded tuff, mudstone, siltstone, and large blocks of microporphyritic basalt seen at Yellow Craig. *Small and rather vulnerable outcrops such as these should be treated with care and not hammered.* Ample opportunity will occur for collecting from the large foreshore outcrop at the next locality.

2. Longskelly Point: Vent and Concentric Structure

Proceed due north across low sand dunes and the beach sand to the wave-cut platform of Longskelly Point. The east end of this platform is an intrusive sheet of black microporphyritic olivine-basalt. In the absence of contacts it is not clear whether the sheet was intruded entirely within the vent or extended into the flanks of the volcano. Note the prominent jointing and poorly formed columns in the hard, fissile basalt. Towards the west end of the wave-cut platform there occurs a concentric structure lying within the vent, possibly caused by collapse. Standing on the basalt plug some 25 m across in the centre of this structure, one can see concentric ridges and hollows formed by alternating hard basalt and soft agglomerate. Here also the greenish vent agglomerate contains fragments of various lithologies. The vent margin lies along a curved hollow where vent agglomerate cuts across Markle basalt lava, the lava distinguished by its numerous large feldspar phenocrysts.

Offshore Islands

At this point it is worth pausing to look at the four islands which enhance this coastline. Lying just offshore, Fidra is a thick sill of microporphyritic olivine-basalt, note the fine columnar structure in the basalt, the natural arch on the far side, and the low raised beach and cave on the near side. To the east the rocky Lamb is probably part of the same columnar basalt sill. Further east still, the rounded Craigleith is an essexite laccolith, and the vertical-cliffed Bass Rock is a phonolite volcanic plug. Also prominent to the south-east is another phonolitic plug forming the conical North Berwick Law.

3. Longskelly Rocks: Markle Basalt and Mugearite Lavas

For the next 800 m the rocks on the foreshore consist of Markle basalt lava, dipping gently to the south. Round the point opposite Fidra, the junction between Markle basalt and the overlying mugearite lava to the south can be traced near H.W.M. Contrast the angular appearance of the grey, fissile, non-porphyritic mugearite with the rounded appearance of the darker grey, crumbly Markle basalt containing numerous large feldspar and small olivine phenocrysts. The upper part of the basalt lava is autobrecciated and has amygdales and calcite veins. The high level of the wave-cut platform suggests formation during a higher post-Glacial sea level rather than at present.

4. Small Intrusive Plug

Located below a 'Power Cable' sign is a neat oval plug of hard black basalt, 5 m by 10 m, intruded into Markle basalt lava. The intrusion has a pale chilled margin which can be traced along the somewhat irregular contact with the lava.

5. Marine Villa: Volcanic Succession.

Towards Marine Villa, due to a change of strike, the volcanic succession of Markle basalt, mugearite and trachytic tuff is traversed in ascending order. Here the mugearite lava is very well exposed, and in it can be seen sparse feldspar phenocrysts, concentric iron-banding with bleached centres, and numerous calcite veins. Note here also the storm beaches

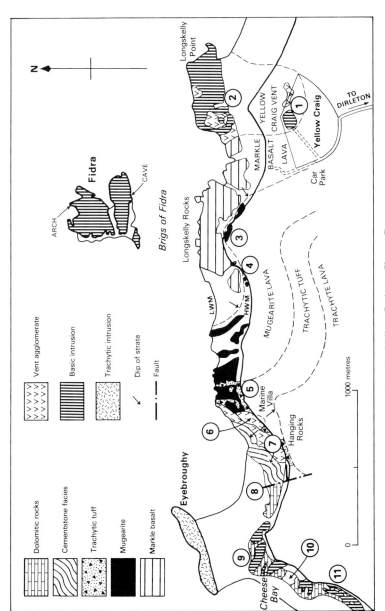

MAP 12. Yellow Craig to Cheese Bay

of black microporphyritic basalt boulders, brought by currents across from Fidra; during exceptionally low tides the connecting Brigs of Fidra may be exposed. Opposite Marine Villa, used by R. L. Stevenson as the location for his short novel *The Pavilion on the Links*, the junction of mugearite lava and overlying red bedded trachytic tuff is repeatedly exposed by a combination of low dip, slight folding and irregular erosion. The irregular slaggy amygdaloidal top of the lava has been preserved here by the overlying tuff. The absence of a bole of red fossil soil indicates that the tuffs were deposited soon after the lava. Sections of the trachytic tuffs in low cliffs show alternation of coarse and fine bands and an agglomeratic base. Slickensided planes with slight movement are indications of the faulting occurring further west.

6. Weaklaw Vent

Just beyond a second 'Power Cable' sign the red bedded tuffs are truncated along a silicified plane, dipping at 30° to the west, well-exposed at H.W.M. and in the low cliffs behind. This is taken as the edge of a small vent, about 100 m across, filled with reddish-brown poorly bedded sandy tuffaceous breccia containing grey cementstone blocks. Along H.W.M. beyond the vent are exposures of soft, yellow, bedded dolomitic tuffs containing blocks of trachyte, some markedly feldspar-phyric.

7. Hanging Rocks: Intrusion Breccia

Intruded along a NE-SW fault separating the trachytic tuffs from cementstone facies sediments is a yellow dolomitic breccia with large hornfelsed shale blocks. The south-east margin of this intrusion breccia is spectacularly displayed in two bluffs as planes dipping at 60° and 45°, which leave the breccia 'hanging' against the bedded volcanic rocks in the cliffs behind. By the caves in the next bluff, 5 m of rotten, purple, vesicular, porphyritic trachyte lava with an irregular base rest on 8 m of purple and cream, bedded trachytic tuff with agglomeratic bands.

8. Cementstone Facies Sediments and Synclinal Ring Structure

From the slopes above the caves there are fine views of gentle folding in bedded sediments on the foreshore. Close examination on descending to the shore shows that these are cementstone facies sediments, consisting of thin red-weathering grey cementstones, some nodular, grey siltstones and mudstones, in which plant fragments and rarely shells may be found. Minor folding and faulting can be discovered within the larger structures. Just to the west, and separated from the sediments by a fault, there is an asymmetric synclinal structure, possibly caused by collapse. Prominent hard dolomitic bands alternating with softer tuffaceous bands pick out dips of up to 40° in the structure.

9. Point Opposite Eyebroughy: Basalt Sill

A thin irregular sill of microporphyritic basalt has been intruded into dolomitic and tuffaceous sediments. The sill, cut by erosion into several parts, displays fine columnar structures varying from horizontal to vertical. Eyebroughy, a rocky tidal islet, consists of trachyte, thought to be intrusive.

10. Cheese Bay: Shrimp Bed

In the bay to the south, which reputedly owes its name to the wreck of a ship laden with cheese, gently folded sediments crop out. A band of hard red-weathering cementstone with estheriids is underlain by dark grey mudstones, black bituminous shales containing ostracods, fish scales and pyritised plants, finely colour-banded shales, and a thin fissile grey silty cementstone. This locality is noted for the occurrence of the shrimp *Tealliocaris woodwardi*, which is particularly abundant in the thin silty cementstone. A list of the numerous species of fish and plants also collected from these beds is given by Clough (1910, p. 207). More recent studies on this locality have been done by Hesselbo and Trewin (1984). Over-collection has obscured the richest beds, but fine specimens of shrimps may be obtained by splitting fragments on the beach.

11. Cheese Bay Sill

Just to the south another microporphyritic basalt sill is similarly intruded into dolomitic sediments. In the bouldery area beyond, prominent isolated stacks of basalt capped by outliers of baked sediments show the development of white trap, druses and other phenomena produced by intrusion of basaltic magma into carbonate rocks. The excursion can be completed by continuing south to Gullane (3 km) from where a service bus goes to Edinburgh, or by returning along the shore to Yellowcraig (4 km).

12. Dirleton Castle: Trachyte Lava

Worthy of a visit in Dirleton Village is the ruined castle built in the 13th to 15th century. The castle (516 839), open all year, is sited on a trachyte crag. The red-purple stained, fine-grained trachyte lava has white feldspar phenocrysts and is typical of the trachyte lavas which form a thick pile in the Garleton Hills, but are represented on the coast only by the lava at Hanging Rocks. The return journey takes one through the charming villages of Gullane, Aberlady and Longniddry to Edinburgh.

A. D. McADAM

GARLETON HILLS VOLCANIC ROCKS

O.S. 1:50000 Sheet 67 Duns and Dunbar
B.G.S. 1:50000 Sheet 33W Haddington
Route: Map 13

CONTEMPORANEOUS with the Lower Carboniferous volcanics that crop out in and around Edinburgh (p. 33), are volcanic rocks which re-appear some 32 km east of the city in the vicinity of North Berwick and the Garleton Hills. The succession is thicker, and with the presence of trachytes, more varied than that of the Arthur's Seat Volcanic Rocks in Edinburgh. The Garleton Hills Volcanic Rocks lie within the Calciferous Sandstone Measures. A generalised succession is as follows:

Trachyte lavas and tuffs	160 m
Basaltic and mugearitic lavas	160 m
Basaltic tuffs	200 m

Whereas the basaltic and mugearitic lavas and the basal ash-beds are well exposed on the coast at North Berwick (p. 88), this excursion is principally concerned with the inland outcrops in the vicinity of the Garleton Hills and Traprain Law. In this region, the basal ashes are thin and largely unexposed, but the basic and trachytic lavas can be easily examined in numerous quarries and natural outcrops. Intrusive phonolite may be examined at Traprain Law, where Pleistocene glaciation has deeply eroded the softer Carboniferous sedimentary rocks and left the tough intrusive rocks as a prominent high-point in the landscape. The excursion also includes one of the late Carboniferous quartz-dolerite dykes (Bangly Hill). A presumed intrusive mass of silica-undersaturated basalt (basanite) containing peridotite inclusions and cut by intrusive tuff is seen at Kidlaw.

The excursion commences among the trachyte lavas of the Garleton Hills, proceeds on to the basic lavas beneath the trachytes in the vicinity of East Linton and then moves south to Traprain Law and finally to Kidlaw, not far from Gifford. Private transport is essential to complete the excursion in one day.

1. Bangly Quarry: Trachytic Lava and Dyke

The quarry (NT 487 752) is reached from a small road leaving the A1 about 2 km east of Gladsmuir. It is being worked for road-metal and lies apparently within a single massive flow of trachyte. The trachyte is strongly porphyritic with feldspar phenocrysts up to 5 mm. Where fresh the matrix is bluish-grey, although much of the trachyte is reddened through oxidation and alteration. The feldspar phenocrysts consist of sodic plagioclase cores, rimmed by alkali feldspar. This zonation is brought out clearly by differential weathering and is readily seen on weathered surfaces. Small pyroxene (hedenbergite) phenocrysts are also present.

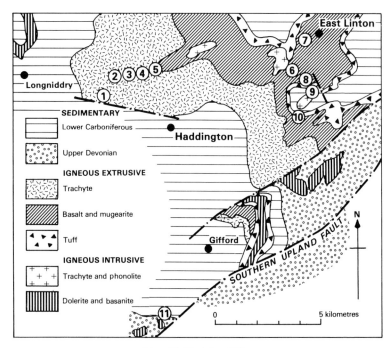

MAP 13. Garleton Hills

The matrix is of fine-grained quartz-trachyte. At the eastern end of the quarry a 4 m dyke of trachybasalt occurs. This dyke is periodically visible in the course of quarrying. Even when obscured by talus, fragments of the dyke rock can be recognized from the presence of large (up to 5 cm) glassy-clear crystals of sanidine.

On the northern wall of the quarry the trachyte is finely jointed and shows abundant signs of crushing. In places the closely jointed trachyte passes into a breccia of trachyte blocks in a fine-grained dark matrix. It is unclear whether the brecciation is wholly due to crushing or whether high-pressure gas-fluxing may have been partly responsible.

2. Bangly Hill: Quartz-dolerite Dyke

Approximately 1 km NNE from Bangly Quarry on the road leading to Phantassie, a small farm road leads north to a hill surmounted by a radio relay station. On the northern side of this hill is an old quarry (493 758) cut into a broad E-W quartz-dolerite dyke with a minimum thickness of 12 m. This dyke is one of the swarm of late Carboniferous (Stephanian) quartz-dolerite dykes and sills, within and adjacent to the Midland Valley. The south wall of the quarry exposes somewhat crushed porphyritic trachyte (similar to that seen in Bangly Quarry) alongside the southern chilled wall of the dyke. The chilled contact of the dolerite against trachyte is well exposed in the south-west corner of the quarry. The chilled facies is very fine-grained with trails of amygdales parallel to the contact wall.

At the eastern end of the quarry, well-developed jointing (crudely columnar) in the dolerite dips at $c.$ 10° S, suggesting that the dyke as a whole has a steep dip ($c.$ 80°) towards the north. The dyke here displays an excellent example of spheroidal weathering. The northern contact of the dolerite is not exposed.

3. Phantassie Hill: Trachyte Lavas and Mineralization

Return to the public road and proceed east to the junction with the A6137. Continue east across the junction on a farm road for 300 m until a gate is reached on the left-hand side, with a prominent escarpment visible across a small field (507 757). This escarpment is composed of one or more thick flows of sub-horizontal trachyte. The trachyte is generally similar to that seen at the last two localities but has zones which are reddened, much altered and cut by veins of baryte. The baryte occurs as rosette-like aggregates of thin tabular crystals coloured pink with hematite. Hematite is not particularly well developed in the veins on this escarpment but was formerly mined in the vicinity, some 200 m across the field to the north-west where the entrance to the old mine-workings can still be seen (513 761).

The trachyte of the escarpment is porphyritic (including plagioclase, alkali feldspar, altered clinopyroxene and scarce apatite phenocrysts) and is, in places, highly vesicular. The freshest samples may be obtained from a shallow hole in the floor of the upper part of the old quarry.

4. View eastwards from the Garleton Hills

From the roadside (509 763) at the entrance to Skid Hill Quarry the view eastwards clearly reveals the relationship between the basic and trachytic lavas of the area. The valley leading away from the viewpoint is a glacial outwash channel which cuts down through the rocky outcrop of the trachytes of the Kae Heughs escarpment into the underlying, poorly exposed basaltic and mugearitic flows forming the valley floor.

5. Skid Hill Quarry: Trachytic Lava

The disused quarry (507 757) appears to be excavated within a single flow of quartz-trachyte some 20 m or more thick. The rock here is massive with no sign of vesiculation. Small hematite veinlets are well exposed cutting the trachyte of the quarry floor. Fresh bluish-grey trachyte, containing sanidine, plagioclase and augite phenocrysts in a matrix of alkali feldspar, quartz, aegirine-augite, magnetite and hematite, can be obtained in the quarry.

6. Pencraig Wood: Trachyte Intrusion

In a small quarry (573 765) beside a lay-by on the north of the A1 road, can be seen the pale purple, non-porphyritic intrusive trachyte which underlies Pencraig Wood. This rock has been exploited for road metal in Markle Mains Quarry (565 770) just to the north.

7. Markle Quarry: Markle Basalt Lava

Some 150 m north of the A1 road, about 1 km west of East Linton, a path leading off alongside an electricity sub-station leads to a disused quarry (583 769). The quarry is excavated in a low escarpment extending north-eastwards from Pencraig Wood, revealing a section through one of the more basic lavas underlying the trachytes. The quarry reveals a 7–8 m thickness of lava, which is non-vesicular in its lower and central parts but which grades into distinctly vesicular material in the topmost 1·5 to 2 m. This is clearly the near-surface facies of a flow of 'aa' type. The flow is remarkable for the abundance of tabular plagioclase phenocrysts in all but its uppermost parts. This distribution may be due either to the gravitational settling of crystals that were denser than the liquid in which they were suspended, or alternatively to late-stage pulses of phenocryst-deficient lava overriding earlier phenocryst-rich material. The lava is much altered and reddened by hematitisation, but reddish-brown pseudomorphs after former olivine phenocrysts and small phenocrysts of magnetite may still be seen in hand-specimen. Apatite microphenocrysts have been recognized in thin-section. The flow is the type locality of Markle basalt (MacGregor 1928), which contains abundant large phenocrysts of plagioclase, subordinate olivine phenocrysts, but no pyroxene phenocrysts. The type is of widespread occurrence in the lower Carboniferous lavas of the Midland Valley.

8. Kippielaw Scarp: Basalt and Mugearite Lavas

The route now continues eastwards across the River Tyne to the junction (593 768) of the A1 and the minor road leading south towards Traprain Farm. Scattered outcrops seen at this junction and in the fields to the south-east are in basalt lavas low in the volcanic succession. At Traprain Farm (592 757), the minor road leading westwards towards Kippielaw Farm should be followed for about 200 m until, beyond a patch of woodland, there is access to a low south-ward-facing escarpment. At this vantage point a good view may be had of the surrounding countryside. To the north rise the prominent phonolitic trachyte plugs of North Berwick Law and Bass Rock and to the west, across the Tyne Valley, are the trachytes of the Garleton Hills. Arthur's Seat can be

seen still farther west where the Lower Carboniferous lavas
re-emerge on the western limb of the Midlothian coalfield.

About 1 km south of the escarpment, the steep-sided
Traprain Law rises out of fields underlain by rocks of the Calciferous Sandstone Measures. These rocks are brought up in
the core of the anticlinal structure created by the Traprain
Law intrusion.

Three or four kilometres beyond Traprain is the fault-line
scarp of the Southern Uplands where barren moorlands
mark the outcrop of the older Lower Palaeozoic shales and
greywackes and contrast with the cultivated farmlands overlying the younger Upper Palaeozoic sediments in the fore-
ground and middle distance.

The mugearite flow near Traprain Farm lies low in the lava
sequence. The lavas themselves are separated from the
underlying Calciferous Sandstone Measures by a horizon of
ashes, correlative with the thick basal ash sequence so well
seen on the foreshore at North Berwick. The ash-horizon
here, however, is much attenuated and largely unexposed; if
time permits it may be examined later in the uncultivated
fields to the west of Kippielaw Farm, around 580 755.

Where first seen the mugearite is a fine-grained, lustrous
and relatively fresh rock with a prominent platy jointing
which, dipping north at less than 5°, indicates the local dip of
the lava sequence. The rock here is non-vesicular. Tabular
phenocrysts of plagioclase occur very sparingly. In thin-section, this rock is seen to consist of flow-aligned oligoclase,
Fe-Ti oxides and altered olivines. Alkali feldspar occurs in-
terstitially and biotite is a prominent accessory mineral.
Progressing west along the scarp front the upper facies of this
flow can be found forming a 20–40 cm thick zone of vesicular
and rubbly material.

Continuing west to a point about 30 m east of a drystone
wall running approximately N–S, one leaves the mugearite
flow and descends on to the upper surface of the underlying
basalt flow. The scoriaceous upper surface of this flow is,
from time to time, revealed by ploughing and loose blocks of
the flow-surface material are normally to be encountered
close to the wall.

This flow is a basalt of Dunsapie type (MacGregor 1928)
characterised by relatively abundant reddened plagioclase

2. Phonolite laccolith, Traprain Law, from Pencraig

phenocrysts, scarcer black augite phenocrysts and brown pseudomorphs after former olivine phenocrysts.

On the west side of the wall good outcrops are seen of the massive central facies of this flow. Continuing west along the front of the escarpment, here about 6 m high, one encounters more coarsely grained basalt, still of Dunsapie type with phenocrysts of all three main silicate phases. The rock is well seen in an old quarry immediately south of Kippielaw Farm. It is likely that this basalt belongs to a second flow of Dunsapie basalt beneath that first encountered, since it becomes more vesicular towards the top of the quarry, which may be close to the flow top.

From Kippielaw Farm one has the choice of either returning along the Traprain Law farm road and then taking transport to Traprain Law quarry or alternatively, walking southwards by the farm track to the quarry.

9. Traprain Law: Phonolite Laccolith

The dome-shaped mass of Traprain Law appears to reflect the form of the upper surface of the intrusion virtually unmodified by erosion. In the large road-metal quarry (584 750) on the north-east side of the hill, a prominent set of joints lies approximately parallel to the contacts. The intrusion is generally believed to have a laccolithic form and to have been responsible for arching up the surrounding sediments and lavas. The phonolite exhibits considerable variety in terms of colour and texture (Tomkeieff 1952). Pronounced flow-banding can be seen on the east face of the quarry, involving layers of grey rock and layers of a pinker, more speckled variety. There is some evidence that the pink bands owe their origin to a slight hydrothermal alteration of the grey. Sedimentary xenoliths, mainly of black shale and sandstone in varying states of assimilation, are common in the intrusion, blocks up to 10 m long having been recovered by Day (1929). Xenoliths of basic igneous rocks, including an unusual analcime-trachybasalt (Tomkeieff 1952) are much scarcer.

The phonolite contains phenocrysts of oligoclase and cryptoperthite with small, scarce phenocrysts of clinopyroxene, apatite and much-oxidized and corroded hornblende. The matrix consists of antiperthite, aegirine-augite, fayalite, sodalite and magnetite. The presence of small quantities of nepheline has also been reported (MacGregor and Ennos 1922). Late crystallising components, largely concentrated into thin veinlets include analcime, calcite, apophyllite and alkali feldspar. Prehnite, pectolite, natrolite, datolite, anhydrite, selenite and stilpnomelane have also been recorded.

The phonolite, though devoid of vesicles on the lower flanks of Traprain, becomes highly vesicular near the summit suggesting that the rock crystallised under near-surface conditions and that the intrusion may even have acted as a feeder for surface extrusions.

10. Balfour Monument: Craiglockhart Basalt and Kulaite Lavas

Take the road east and then south of Traprain Law to the minor road junction (603 739) and then travel westwards to the monument set on a prominent north-facing lava escarpment (575 737). Just as at the Kippielaw escarpment, the arable land between the escarpment and the steep contact wall of the Traprain intrusion lies on Calciferous Sandstone Measures sedimentary rocks.

The lava forming the main scarp feature here is some 15 m thick and shows a roughly columnar jointing pattern. It is an ankaramitic basalt, rich in large augite crystals (up to 1 cm) and conspicuous brown pseudomorphs after olivine (up to 0·5 cm). This rock, following MacGregor's (1928) classification, is a basalt of Craiglockhart type.

A subordinate scarp feature, below and some way east of the monument, is formed from an underlying trachybasaltic flow. This much decomposed rock, which has been called a kulaite, contains a high concentration of pseudomorphed (oxidised) hornblende phenocrysts. In the fine-grained matrix, plagioclase and analcime are among the least altered components.

11. Kidlaw Quarry: Tuffs, Analcime-basanite Intrusion and Peridotite (Lherzolite) Inclusions

This locality, some 5 km south-west of Gifford and about 13 km south-west of Traprain Law, is reached by a sunken grassy track leading from the junction of the two minor roads near Kidlaw (506 642) into the disused quarry. On entering the quarry, small outcrops of reddish tuff may be seen on the right-hand bank beside the path. These consist of small (<5 mm) particles of what appear to be altered volcanic glass. These scoria fragments are very vesicular, often showing deformed and streaked-out vesicles. The matrix between the volcanic fragments consists largely of angular quartz grains and lesser amounts of microcline.

The quarry itself, however, is mainly cut into a fine-grained tough and well-jointed analcime-basanite (or monchiquitic basalt). From the non-vesicular nature of the mass it is likely to be a hypabyssal intrusion although there is no clear guide to the overall form. Clough *et al.* (1910) considered it to be a sill intruded into the Calciferous Sandstone Measures though, on the basis of a vertical contact between tuff and basanite exposed during quarrying operations in the 1920's, Simpson (1928) has suggested that it is a plug in a vent. The rock is slightly porphyritic, carrying small scattered phenocrysts of olivine, augite and plagioclase. The groundmass is composed of augite, magnetite, biotite, plagioclase and alkali feldspar with analcime forming poikilitic patches up to 2 mm across. The latter accounts for the speckled appearance of many of the weathered rock surfaces.

The intrusion is of interest in that it contains relatively abundant ultrabasic 'nodules'. Generally less than 5 cm across and consisting of olivine, enstatite, diopside and spinel in varying stages of alteration, they can be best described as altered spinel lherzolites. On weathered surfaces they 'weather in' to form shallow hollows, often with an associated set of radial cracks in the adjacent host rock.

In the central part of the quarry wall a small sheet (about 20 cm thick) of intrusive tuff cuts the basanite. The clasts in this greenish tuff are of varied lithologies, but consist largely of sandstone and biotite-granite, in a matrix composed mainly of quartz grains.

The intrusive tuff is quite dissimilar to the red tuff which outcrops on the south side of the quarry. It is less well sorted in terms of grain-size and variety of components and lacks the opaque fragments of volcanic rock that characterise the red tuff. The fragments of biotite-granite which it contains are of some interest: they possibly have some connection with the granitic mass of probably Lower Old Red Sandstone age exposed some 500 m to the ESE, on the southern side of the Southern Upland Fault (Simpson 1928).

B. G. J. UPTON and R. MACDONALD

DUNBAR

O.S. 1:50000 Sheet 67 Duns & Dunbar
B.G.S. 1:50000 Sheet 33E Dunbar
Route: Maps 14 and 15

THE main object of the excursions is to study volcanic necks (pipes) exposed in the cliffs and on the intertidal wavecut platform. These structures mark the sites of former underground channels which fed early Carboniferous (Dinantian) volcanoes. Erosion has since removed the volcanoes and some thickness of the rocks beneath them so that the pipes are now seen at various levels below the original surface of eruption. The rocks in them consist mainly of lithified volcanic ash (tuffs), with subordinate agglomerates and alkali-basaltic intrusions, and they are surrounded by the sediments of Upper Old Red Sandstone and Lower Carboniferous age through which the original feeder channels penetrated. At the time of the volcanism, these sediments were probably so young that they still contained water. Moreover, the volcanoes were erupted on a surface covered by shallow sea or lagoon, so that water from surface or sediments gained access to the ascending molten magma column and gave rise to violently explosive (phreatomagmatic) activity. Modern comparison is thus with maars or ash-rings like early Surtsey (Walker and Croasdale 1972) rather than with Strombolian basaltic cinder cones found in inland areas.

Two processes have been recognized in the emplacement of the pipes at Dunbar (Francis 1962). In the first eruptive phase the pipes are assumed to have been drilled through the sediments by a gas-propelled stream advancing above the molten magma column and containing fragments of ragged-edged, chilled basalt and of sediments broken by the stream from the walls of the channels. Remnants of the process are now to be seen at pipe margins where adjacent sediments are shattered and intimately penetrated by the gas-driven ash and where blocks and fragments show flow-orientation. The

119

process is also seen in small ring-structures (cryptovolcanic) representing upward drillings which were arrested before reaching the surface. In the second phase, which followed when eruption ceased, bedded ash (now tuff) at or near the contemporaneous surface subsided into the feeding channels, sometimes to depths of hundreds of metres. The bedding structures provide evidence not only of ash-fall at the surface, but also of flow ranging from lateral base-surge engendered by violent eruption to mass debris flows down inner flanks of the original sub-aerial ash-rings. The eventual preservation of the layering ranges from relatively intact to wholly collapsed, depending partly on how loose the ash was at the time and partly on the depth to which it subsided. Because of the subsidence the margins of such pipes are commonly ring-faults, and the process of down-drag is also reflected in the attitude of the sediments adjacent to those faulted margins. Thus, two different kinds of ash from the same volcanoes are brought together at one level—the material subsided from the surface at the centre of the pipes—and the deeper-seated intrusional material still in place at the margins.

The sediments and pipes are traversed by a group of ENE quartz-dolerite dykes of Stephanian age, best seen at Belhaven and forming offshore skerries farther east. The dykes and the earlier tuffs are reddened to greater or lesser degree, reflecting the colouration of the surrounding sediments. This feature at Dunbar, and elsewhere, has been attributed by Lorenz (1972) to circulation of ground-water from the sediments, leading to oxidation of the iron content in the volcanic rocks.

The itinerary below is designed for two excursions, one from Belhaven to the Parade (p. 122) and the other around Dunbar itself (p. 127). However, if only one day is available it is suggested that they can be combined by starting at Belhaven Point (locs. 1, 2), traversing the Parade Neck at the foot of the cliffs (locs. 4, 5, 6), ascending by steps to the road, walking from there to the harbour area (locs. 7, 8, 9) and thence south-eastward near high water mark (H.W.M.) (locs. 11, 12, 13). The total walking distance is about 6 km, ending a similar distance by road from the starting point. In a race against the tide, this sequence might be varied in the

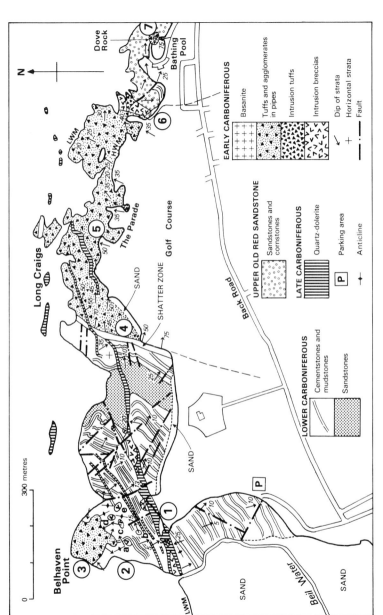

MAP 14. Belhaven and the Parade

knowledge that some of the harbour exposures (7, 8) can be seen when most others are covered by the sea.

There are frequent train and Lowland Scottish service buses from Edinburgh to Dunbar. For excursions by road, the main parking area for cars and buses is near the Barracks, in Dunbar, though limited car parking can also be found near the beach at Belhaven and at Victoria Harbour in Dunbar.

Excursion A—Belhaven and the Parade
(Route: Map 14)

Starting from the car-parking area at Belhaven Beach (NT 662 787) the walking distance is about 2 km ending in a steep flight of steps up from the beach behind the Bathing Pool. It is a similar distance returning to the car park along Back Road or, preferably, along the Parade itself, which offers fine vantage points down to the foreshore.

1. Linear Breccia and Quartz-dolerite Dyke

The sediments at Belhaven consist mainly of rhythmic alternations of Lower Carboniferous cementstones and mudstones with one thick bed of sandstone. They dip generally south-eastwards. They are traversed at H.W.M. by an ENE linear volcanic breccia which is irregularly intruded by the widest of the local quartz-dolerite dykes. Its margins are defined by faults inclined towards one another and locally flanked inside by blocks which are aligned parallel to the margins. Eastwards the faults diverge, the southern having a displacement of about 30 m. At its western extremity the breccia includes large blebs of 'white trap'. The breccia, which has two small cryptovolcanic ring structures emplaced along the northern bounding fracture, is assumed to belong to the early Carboniferous volcanism.

2. Cryptovolcanic Ring Structures

Five small areas of breccia (a-e, Map 14) are referred to as ring structures, though they tend to be oval rather than circular in plan. In some places their contacts with the surrounding sedimentary rocks are vertical or steeply inclined inwards; in other places an impression is gained of high-angled outward dip though this is nowhere capable of demonstration. The breccias consist mainly of local cementstones and marls. Peripherally the flat surfaces and longer axes of the blocks become orientated with the margins. At the centre, however, the blocks are usually completely jumbled, though in one ring (e) the centre consists of relatively undisturbed cementstones and marls. Two rings (b, d) contain red tuffs which appear to penetrate the breccias; they are most prominent at the margins, but also (c) form dykes and pods associated with veins and blebs of decomposed chilled basalt ('white trap').

Maufe (in Clough *et al.* 1910, p. 90) thought that they were necks which pierced low domes and were contemporaneous with, and overlapped by the sediments. However, they are now believed to be incipient pipes which never reached the surface. Those margins which show apparent overlap merely reflect the upwards pressure of the gas-tuff stream, while the inwardly-inclined fractured margins represent a slightly lower erosional level in funnel-shaped fractures, with the marginally orientated blocks evidencing a variety of flow-banding.

3. Belhaven Point Neck

The margin of the neck is irregular in outline. To east and west, where the irregularity is least prominent, the adjacent sediments are turned down towards the margin, but where the neck extends southward the sediments are either horizontal or dip away from the contact. The neck filling ranges in grade from fine-grained tuffs to lapilli-tuffs and has a red colour mottled by yellow and green juvenile basaltic material. Near the margin the tuffs also contain blocks of cementstone and sandstone similar to the country rocks outside. The tuffs have an unbedded appearance except for what seems to be a vertically stratified discrete raft, measuring 2.5×7.5 m, near the centre of the neck. Two small bosses, measuring 3.5×6 m and 7.5×7.5 m, to south and centre respectively, are of basanite similar to the other vent intrusions of the district, though they are partially carbonated.

4. Parade Neck: West Margin

The largest neck in the area, nearly 1 km in diameter, takes its name from the promenade along the top of the cliffs in which it is well exposed. The cementstones immediately outside the neck are nearly flat at L.W.M., but at H.W.M. they dip in towards the margin at progressively higher angles until they pass into a zone 9 to 15 m wide in which the sediments are highly inclined or vertical and show signs of shattering and squeezing out. Inside the neck also, the easterly dip of the bedded tuffs becomes steepest adjacent to this zone, though in places the bedded tuffs appear to pass into massive tuffs containing blocks of sedimentary rock. In the cliff about 15 m inside the margin is a spectacular intrusion of sandstone within the tuffs. It is partly sill, partly dyke, arranged in 'step-and-stair', but the internal layering, which resembles bedding, remains parallel to the enclosing walls. This, together with off-shoots of sandstone which peter out at various angles into the tuffs, shows the body to be intrusive.

Still nearer to the western margin of the neck a 2 m dyke of mottled grey and purple sandstone can be traced northwards, first thinning out for a short distance, then forming pods inside a line of crush and later reappearing as a sill which seems in ground plan to change horizon through the bedded tuffs. An offshoot dyke, 25 to 40 cm thick, is intruded westwards to cut the vent-marginal zone of crushed and inwardly down-turned sediments. The main dyke contains some magmatic debris and two separate elements of vertical flow-banding, one of which crosses the other obliquely in much the same way as current bedding in sedimentary rocks. At H.W.M. the main dyke pinches out more abruptly, though its course is continued into the cliff by a line of disturbance. On the western side of the dyke there is another 3 m intrusion, consisting of a purple sandy siltstone banded with streaky, purple and yellow tuff. At first sight this seems to be a large xenolith of bedded tuffaceous sediment dipping westward at 65°–85° and crumpled and faulted on a small scale. On closer examination, however, the streaky yellow layers in the tuff are seen to be flow-banded and intrusive into the siltstone and the adjacent dyke of sandstone. The flow-banding of yellow basaltic lapilli and the 'bedding' of the siltstone, moreover, remain orientated parallel to the margins of the mass as it pinches out southwards. It is suggestive of two, if not three, successive pulses of intrusion hereabouts.

5. Parade Neck: Bedded Tuffs and Sandstone Dykes

Along the shore and in the cliffs the vent-filling consists of bedded reddish and brown tuffs ranging from fine-grained to lapilli-tuffs. They consist of variable proportions of two main components. One is a sandstone suite seen in thin section to consist mainly of quartz grains with subordinate amounts of orthoclase, microcline, plagioclase and mica: the other is basaltic and consists partly of crystalline material, but more abundantly of yellow vesicular glass (refractive index exceeding 1·54 and usually replaced by carbonate, kaolinite or turbid decomposition products). Some of the glassy fragments appear to have enclosed grains of quartz. In some of the fine layers the glass is elongated parallel to the bedding, giving rise to a macroscopic vitroclastic texture. Blocks of basalt, tuff, indurated cementstone, cornstone, sandstone and shale ranging in diameter up to 1·2 m, but averaging about 12 cm, are scattered throughout. Local disruption of the subjacent layering and sagging in the beds a little farther below testify to their emplacement as bombs: some of the basaltic bombs, moreover, are grouped in a manner suggesting spatter. However, although the tuffs near the western margin appear to be of similar ash-fall origin, the cross-bedding throughout the remainder of the neck is on a scale which is entirely consistent with deposition from a series of base-surges driven from an eruptive source or sources located to north-east, east or south-east (Leys 1982).

The tuffs are crossed by a roughly rectilinear pattern of master joints trending north-east and north-west. The younger quartz-dolerite dykes have been emplaced along the fractures, as have many further sandstone dykes laminated parallel to their high-angled enclosing walls. This lamination—an alignment of micas—is less pronounced at the centres of the dykes than at the margins. Some dykes are cemented by, or pass laterally into carbonate. The joint system and the sandstone intrusions are believed to date from the subsidence stage of the Parade Neck.

6. Parade Neck: Eastern Margin

The eastern margin is outlined by a boulder-strewn trench, narrowing northwards and containing a partially exposed band of green and purple streaky rock which is up to 1 m thick and is inclined westwards into the neck at 60°. This appears to be fault-gouge rather than flow-banding. Inside the margin the tuffs display an intricate pattern of small-scale faulting, but there is no local breakdown of bedding as there is in the west. In further contrast the dip continues unchanged up to the edge of the neck where the tuffs are laced with anastomosing veins of carbonate and/or hematite which have a sub-parallel alignment with the neck margin. Such veining is characteristic of the inner linings of pipes which have undergone subsidence and is presumed to have formed during that process. At high water mark the relationship of the neck to the sediments is obscured by sand and shingle, but to the south-east a junction is exposed in the cliff alongside the path, where it is marked by a block of false-bedded sandstone 1 m wide, narrowing downwards and tilted at 70° away from the hematite-veined tuffs.

Outside the margin the massive sandstone is diced by small-scale fractures, and the blocks so formed are dislocated and recemented by sand apparently derived from the breakdown of the same beds. The bulk composition of the rock is thus unchanged, but the large constituent blocks can be picked out on weathered surfaces by slight differences in coarseness, colour and orientation. An irregular fracture plane separates this slightly brecciated zone from the undisturbed massive sandstone to the east. The sandstones inside and immediately outside the brecciated zone have rough carious surfaces showing anastomosing patterns of grooves and ridges. They result from fracture during the volcanism and from the filtering and forcing of fine sand along the fractures by gas action.

The brecciated zone is traversed by a dyke of intruded tuff, about 60 m long, tapering from 15 m to 9 m in width as it is followed north-eastwards to low water mark. It is cut off to the west by the gouge at the east margin of the neck and traversed by a north-westerly fault which has a landward down-throw. The outcrop of the tuff dyke is shifted by this fault in a direction which indicates that the dyke is inclined south-eastwards. The tuff is a green, or patchily red, well-mixed rock full of basaltic lapilli. Against the north-western wall of the mass the lapilli are orientated to display flow-banding. The tuff may represent an apophysis, intruded into

Upper Old Red Sandstone, of the material which filled the vent at its pre-subsidence level.

Excursion B—Dunbar
(Route: Map 15)

From the car parking areas at the Barracks (677 791) or Victoria Harbour (679 793), the walking distance is about 4 km (3 km if the Dove Rock is excluded), with 2 km to walk back through the town to the starting point.

7. Dove Rock

Dove Rock is a small plug of basanite surrounded by a narrow inner zone of tuff and an outer zone of partly brecciated inwardly dipping sandstone bounded by a ring fracture. Further incipient ring fractures are seen beyond it. As similar rocks and structures can be seen elsewhere, and as the bathing pool makes access difficult, it is suggested that if time is short both this locality and the seaward side of Castle Rocks could be omitted.

FIG 15. Dunbar Castle

8. Castle Rocks

The neck at Castle Rocks straddles the entrance to the New (Victoria) Harbour (Figure 15), but the margin is accessible at only one locality, just south of the entrance. Even here it is partially obscured by the wall of the old castle, where shattered indurated sandstones dip westward towards the neck. The tuff, which can be examined north of the harbour is red and green and contains evenly distributed lapilli of basalt and older tuffs up to 2 or 3 cm in diameter. It is coarsest to the south-east where there are blocks of fine-grained basalt, up to 30 cm across. The tuffs are indurated by basanite dykes and traversed by red veins containing a central portion of calcite and chalcedony and an outer lining of hematite.

9. The Battery

The Battery is built on a columnar, reddened, decomposed porphyritic basalt (Figure 16) which appears to be conformably underlain by bedded tuffs. It resembles early Carboniferous lavas cropping out 1·5 km to the east (Clough *et al.* 1910, pp. 91, 105–6) rather than the basanites of the minor intrusions associated with the necks. Neither the basalt nor the underlying tuff appears to lie within the Old Harbour Neck (see below) and their stratigraphical position is obscure within a faulted sequence of both Old Red Sandstone and Carboniferous sediments.

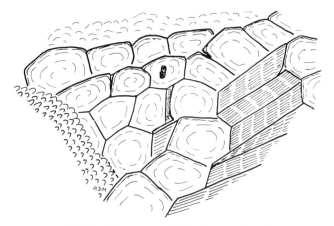

Fɪɢ 16. Columnar basalt, The Battery, Dunbar

10. Old Harbour Neck

The neck underlying the Old Harbour is most clearly delineated on its eastern side where the flanking sandstones

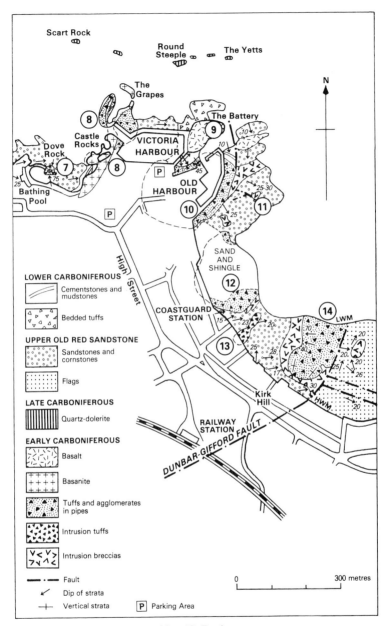

Map 15. Dunbar

form a wall rising above the volcanic rocks. This wall, which inclines in towards the neck at between 50° and 60°, is vertically fluted and polished and represents a plane of movement cutting off the bedding. Veins of intrusion tuff can be seen in the sandstone. Followed seawards, the margin swings west beneath the Old Harbour wall and reappears between the two harbours where it has a south-westerly trend. Beneath the drawbridge on the east wall of Victoria Harbour the outer flanking sediments comprise red marls and cement-stones with interbedded yellow and green tuffs. They are crumpled and tilted steeply towards the neck, swinging round from there to dip conformably northward beneath a basalt underlying the Battery. South of the inter-harbour area the neck margin is built over, but a few exposures of tuff can still be seen west and south of the Old and Victoria harbours respectively.

The neck filling consists of red or, locally, green lapilli-tuffs which are bedded in the north and west, where they strike parallel to the walls and dip inwards at angles ranging from 45° to vertical. East of the Old Harbour wall, however, they have a heterogeneous aspect. This derives partly from the presence, close to the margin, of basaltic blocks and masses of country rock up to 2·5 m in diameter, and partly from the breakdown of original bedding. The bedded relics—some of them intensely crumpled—do not form discrete blocks, but merge instead into an apparently structureless rock. The peripheral tuffs are laced by anastomosing veinlets of hematite and there are, in addition, sills and dykes of similar material up to 60 cm thick. A linear breccia lies to the east of the neck. It has a north-easterly alignment decreasing in width as it is traced from the margin towards low water mark. Like the linear breccia at Belhaven it is derived from the local sediments (sandstones in this instance); it occupies a faulted trough and in places contains marginally orientated blocks. By way of contrast, however, it appears to be related to the adjacent neck, for there is no well defined margin between the two, and the western part of the breccia is penetrated by red tuffs which are similar to the unbedded variety in the neck. The sandstones in the breccia and along the neck margin show typical carious weathering as described from the eastern margin of the Parade Neck.

11. Cryptovolcanic Ring Structures

Two ring structures are exposed to the east of the Old Harbour Neck. The northern is emplaced along a fracture radial to the neck and consists of blocks of local sandstone penetrated by veins of red tuff. Here and in the southern structure the margins are outlined in part by vertically aligned blocks of sandstone.

12. Coastguard Station Neck

This neck, like that of the Old Harbour, rimmed by massive sandstone. Where the margin is continuously exposed on the south it has a regular curving outline and is inclined inwards at 70–80°. Long slices of sandstone, apparently detached from the walls, are now separated from the parent mass of country rock by a narrow zone of unbedded red tuff. The neck filling also resembles that at the Old Harbour in its patchy red and green colour, random scatter of bombs, marginal plexus of red hematitic veins and nearly vertical bedding which strikes parallel to the walls in some places, but in others breaks down to a chaotic arrangement of fragments.

13. Tuff Dyke

This intrusion has a north-easterly trend. Its extent at H.W.M. is obscured by sand, but where first seen it is about 12 m wide narrowing seawards to between 2 and 4 m, finally wedging out in an easterly direction among beds of massive sandstone. The tuff is red with patches of green and yellow basalt and a few bombs of crystalline material. Near the margins it is enriched with fragments of local sandstone up to 30 cm long, and arranged with their long axes parallel to the sides of the dyke. Hair fractures, picked out by red hematite, traverse the steep irregular sandstone walls and the finer constituents of the tuff penetrate raggedly for short distances along these. It is supposed that although the intrusion is not continuous with the Coastguard Station Neck and its filling is differently constituted, the two bodies may have been connected at a lower level before the subsidence of the neck.

14. Kirk Hill Neck

The Kirk Hill Neck is cut off to the east by the Dunbar-Gifford Fault, but to west and south the margin is vertical and has an irregular outline. The neck filling is again similar to the tuffs of the Old Harbour and bedding is more apparent towards the margins than at the centre. The strike of the bedding is approximately parallel to the neck margin to east and west, but adjacent to the southern margin the strike is variable. The bedding is vertical in the east, but dips westwards away from the centre of the neck at 40–70° in the west. In the north-western part of the neck there is a raft of sandstone measuring 2.5×6 m and south-west of the raft there is a 30 cm dyke of sandstone. The latter does not contain flow-banding like the dykes of the Parade Neck. At the indented south margin, tongues of red tuff penetrate the brecciated sandstone wall-rock and the yellow lapilli in this tuff are clearly aligned in flow structure against the sandstone.

E. H. FRANCIS

CATCRAIG

O.S. 1:50000 Sheet 67 Duns & Dunbar
B.G.S. 1:50000 Sheet 33E Dunbar
Route: Map 16

THE fine coastal section at Catcraig exposes the Dinantian limestone-bearing strata of the Lower Limestone Group and the topmost Calciferous Sandstone Measures. The sediments are cyclical, with the thick fossiliferous limestone and calcareous mudstones overlain by deltaic mudstone-siltstone-sandstone sequences and underlain by a thin coal or coal position on a seatearth. The Calciferous Sandstone Measure-Lower Limestone Group boundary is taken at the base of the Upper Longcraig Limestone. The beds below belong to the Brigantian Stage (P_1) and the VF miospore zone, the higher beds to the P_2 goniatite zone and the F-NC miospore zone (Francis *in* Craig 1983, Davies *in* Anon, 1972).

The general succession at Catcraig is:

LOWER LIMESTONE GROUP

		metres
	Massive current-bedded sandstone	
8, 9	BARNS NESS LIMESTONE (= DRYBURNFOOT LIMESTONE	1
	Mainly sandstone, mudstone	10
7	CHAPEL POINT LIMESTONE	3
	Coal horizon and seatclay	0.2
	Sandstone, mudstones, and obscured strata	27
6	UPPER SKATERAW LIMESTONE	0.5
	Calcareous mudstone	1.5
5	MIDDLE SKATERAW LIMESTONE	4
	Thin coal and seatclay	0.1
	Mudstone	3
4	LOWER SKATERAW LIMESTONE	1
	Sandstone and mudstone	5
3	UPPER LONGCRAIG LIMESTONE	6

CALCIFEROUS SANDSTONE MEASURES

	Thin coal and seatclay	0.1
	Mudstone	2

		metres
2	MIDDLE LONGCRAIG LIMESTONE	1.2
	Sandstone	1.5
	Mudstone	0.5
1	LOWER LONGCRAIG LIMESTONE	

The beds lie south of the Southern Upland Fault in the Dunbar Basin. They have a gentle dip to the east, complicated by minor faulting. Because the limestones are accessible they were worked from the late 18th century and burnt for agricultural lime at the Catcraig Limekiln. Now they are exploited in the huge opencast quarries to supply the Dunbar Cement Works of Blue Circle Industries plc, whose chimney and kiln dominate the skyline. It is the Upper Longcraig and Middle Skateraw Limestones that are used together with some of the intervening mudstones. Geological visitors wishing to study the excellent sections in the opencast site should write to the General Works Manager.

Access to the coastal section is obtained from the new A1 road. Turn seaward at the west end of the cement works, signposted East Barns. Turn right along the old A1 taking either the first left to the White Sands car park or second left to Barns Ness Lighthouse caravan site and car park. The area has been laid out as a nature trail by East Lothian District Council. A booklet is available and explanatory notices and geological maps are displayed in the limekiln (Figure 17). The limestone horizons can be located by concrete marker-pillars, numbered as in the above section. The starting point for the excursion is at the old Catcraig limekiln. The excursion takes at least half a day, longer if detailed collecting is included, and is preferably done when the tide is not high.

1. Lower Longcraig Limestone

This limestone is not exposed in the section but is well-known from boreholes.

2. Middle Longcraig Limestone

The lowest beds in the section are seen opposite the old limekiln where the Middle Longcraig Limestone forms an extensive wave cut platform along the shore. This light-grey, highly nodular and often crinoidal limestone has in places a

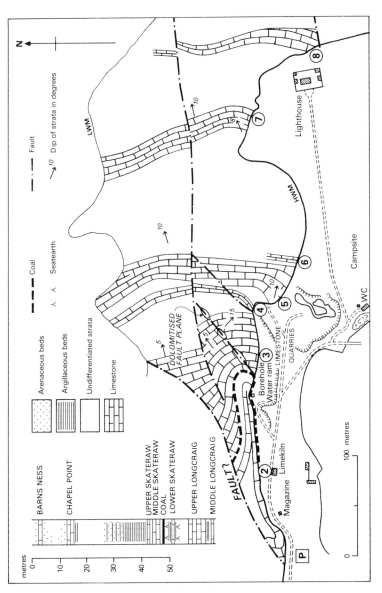

MAP 16. Catcraig

Legend (top):

BARNS NESS

CHAPEL POINT

UPPER SKATERAW
MIDDLE SKATERAW
COAL
LOWER SKATERAW

UPPER LONGCRAIG

MIDDLE LONGCRAIG

metres
0
10
20
30
40
50

Arenaceous beds

Argillaceous beds

Undifferentiated strata

Limestone

Coal

Seatearth

Fault

↗10 Dip of strata in degrees

N

LWM

HWM

Lighthouse

Campsite

WC

LIMESTONE
QUARRIES

Borehole
Water ram

DOLOMITISED
FAULT PLANE

FAULT?

Magazine
Limekiln

P

0   100 metres

Alternate layers of
coal & limestone

Coal brought from b
moorings to kiln he

Lime drawn off
and loaded on
to carts

CATCRAIG LIMEKILN

FIG 17. Catcraig Limekiln

yellow dolomitised upper surface marked by possible glacial striations subparallel with the shore. The limestone rests on sandy beds, seen near the water outlet at the western end of the section, in which the trace fossil *Zoophycos* and U-shaped tubes occur.

The Middle Longcraig Limestone contains excellent specimens of the corals *Lithostrotion junceum* and *L. pauciradiale* particularly near the hydraulic ram, along with the brachiopods *Eomarginifera*, *Spirifer* and *Composita*, with bryozoan debris between the nodules. The upper surface of this limestone is indented with striking basin-shaped hollows about 1 m across and more-or-less evenly spaced. These potholes are of Carboniferous age since they are partially filled in by overlying fireclay and might represent the sites of now-vanished Carboniferous forest trees. The absence of the deltaic part of the cycle might be partly responsible for this. The thin coal seam can be seen in the low cliff, with *Stigmaria* and rootlets visible in the seatclays.

The overlying mudstone forming an elongated shelf has beds rich in the productoid brachiopod *Eomarginifera* and the bivalve *Streblopteria*. Other horizons have copious debris of small crinoids.

3. Upper Longcraig Limestone

The 6 m thick pale grey Upper Longcraig Limestone, above the mudstone, is exposed along the shore. A band, 25 cm thick, about 1 m below the top of the limestone, composed entirely of the coral *Koninckophyllum*, is readily distinguished. This limestone is also exposed inland, in the quarries near the limekilns, where it is very hard, dolomitised, and in places highly brecciated. Irregular undulating surfaces occur within the limestone and some surfaces are covered with dolomite crystals. The overlying mudstone contains plant fragments.

From the hydraulic ram can be seen standing up as a distinct wall resembling a dyke, a dolomitised fault striking 54°E. The fault is of small displacement and is not dolomitised continuously along its length. Close to the fault some very large crinoid stems are exposed on the surface of the limestone.

4. Lower Skateraw Limestone

The Lower Skateraw Limestone, only about a metre thick, is seen on the shore just south of the small headland. It is medium to brownish-grey and fine-grained. Crinoid ossicles are abundant and the limestone is distinguished by the presence of *Gigantoproductus*. Overlying this is a poorly exposed mudstone, seatearth and coal sequence.

5, 6. Middle and Upper Skateraw Limestones

The next cycle begins with the distinctive Middle Skateraw Limestone, which forms a broad shelf below the east car park. This 4 m thick limestone is crinoidal and often nodular. It is distinguished by a 25 cm thick band with innumerable specimens of the foraminiferid *Saccaminopsis* seen as orange or brown spheres 2–3 mm in diameter with a calcitic infilling. Colonies of the flat and discoidal or bun-shaped stromatoporoid *Chaetetes* may be seen at the base of the limestone.

The calcareous mudstone above the Middle Skateraw Limestone is replete with ironstone nodules and is exceptionally fossiliferous with abundant brachiopods, especially *Eomarginifera*, bivalves, the trilobite *Paladin eichwaldi*, solitary corals (including some type species) and crinoid stems and plates. Plates of the crinoid *Parazeacrinites konincki* from this locality were the subject of a detailed taphonomic study by Whyte (1973, 1982). According to Whyte this mudstone and the overlying Upper Skateraw Limestone formed a current-influenced NW-SE trending mudbank with a palaeorelief of up to 20 m. The Upper Skateraw Limestone (6) is pale brown on weathered surfaces. It is here only 50 cm thick and poorly exposed. It contains many hematised nodules.

In the bay to the east the beds above the mudstones are obsured by beach deposits. Towards the lighthouse are ledges of thin sandstone interleaved with fissile mudstone, with abundant surface grazing traces. Rare septarian nodules are present in the mudstones.

7. Chapel Point Limestone

The 3 m thick Chapel Point Limestone which begins the next cycle is encountered west of the lighthouse. It is brownish yellow, highly crinoidal, heavily bioturbated and marked by a diverse succession of abundant trace fossils. Towards the base are numerous *Rhizocorallium*, U-shaped horizontal traces up to 50 cm long, and often of sinuous form. Above these are concentric swirling 'cocks-tails' of *Zoophycos cauda-galli*, the grazing traces of some unknown invertebrate. At some horizons are the open horizontal burrows, sometimes branched, of *Thalassinoides*, together with some fan-shaped traces. At the top of the limestone, as it grades into the overlying sandstone, are giant vertical U-shaped tubes of *Diplocraterion*.

8, 9. Barns Ness Limestone, Dryburnfoot Limestone

Overlying the Chapel Point Limestone on the shore opposite the lighthouse is a thick sandstone sequence which includes a sandy limestone, the Barns Ness Limestone. Borehole evidence suggests that this and the Dryburnfoot Limestone are the same and not separate horizons. The

3. Limestones and mudstones, Lower Limestone Group, cut by basalt dyke and overlain by glacial deposits, Oxwellmains North Quarry

sandstones, coarse to fine, are often current-bedded with large spherical concretions, probably marking a deltaic influx over a shallow nearshore lime-mud sea.

The pipeline east of the lighthouse marks a convenient limit to this excursion.

E. N. K. CLARKSON

PEASE BAY TO COVE

O.S. 1:50000 Sheet 67 Duns & Dunbar
B.G.S. 1:50000 Sheet 34 Eyemouth
Route: Map 17

THE Pease Bay to Cove sequence presents a conformable succession passing up from Upper Old Red Sandstone facies into Carboniferous facies of the Calciferous Sandstone Measures. This transition almost certainly lies well above the Carboniferous-Devonian boundary for, though the first marine bands contain the oldest fully marine horizons in the Scottish Carboniferous, they are of Asbian age, well up in the Viséan. These bands indicate the beginning of the end of desert-fluviatite conditions which had persisted from the early Devonian, and in central Scotland since the middle Silurian (Mykura, Francis *in* Craig 1983).

Pease Bay, a sandy bay dramatically rimmed by Upper Old Red Sandstone cliffs, lies some 1·5 km off the A1 at Cockburnspath, which can be reached by Lowland Scottish service buses. Cars and coaches can be taken with care from the village and down the very steep 300 m track to the car park by the ford before the Pease Bay Caravan Park. The excursion is 2 km along the shore, taking a good half day.

The strata, well exposed in the foreshore and cliff sections, have a general dip to north or NNW, commonly 20° but increasing to 60° when affected by faulting. The succession, modified from Clough *et al.* (1910), is numbered according to the localities to be visited:

		metres
13	Bilsdean Sandstone	14
12	Mudstone with 0·3 m thick Cove Oil-shale	20
11	Cove Harbour Sandstone	26
	Sandstone and shale	8
10	Cove Upper Marine Band	0.4
	Sandstone, mudstone, clay, seatclay	19
10	Cove Lower Marine Band	0.4

140

	Sandstone, mudstone, clay, seatclay with *Cardiopteris*	
	shale-band	32
9	Heathery Heugh Sandstone	55
8	Purple-red and grey marls, including thin coals	32
7	Kip Carle Sandstone	
	(Strata cut out by Cove Fault)	
	Cementstone, conglomerates, sandstone, shales,	
	greenish and purplish cementstones	25+
6	Horse Road Sandstone	43
5	Calcareous sandstone band with *Sanguinolites*	0.4
	Cementstone and shale	17
4	Eastern Hole Conglomerate	0.4
1–3	Upper Old Red Sandstone (cornstones and cross-bedded	
	red sandstones)	80+

1. Greenheugh Point (NT 799 710, Map 18) Upper Old Red Sandstone

There is a good sequence of upper Old Red Sandstone sediments to the east of Pease Bay. Approximately 1 km from the bay a large fallen block was found crowded with largely intact specimens of the fish *Bothriolepis* which had been trapped in a drying-out pond. Much of this material is preserved in the Royal Museum of Scotland.

2. Deil's Hole: Upper Old Red Sandstone

Across the sands, the high red cliff at the northern end of Pease Bay is composed of alternating laminar and cross-bedded red sandstones, dipping 17°N. At the base is fine trough cross-stratification, the troughs trending southwards and visible both in section and from the upper surface. These beds were rapidly deposited by fast-flowing currents in distributary channels which frequently eroded earlier filled channels. The intervening layered sediments with green reduction spots in places, are flood-plain deposits.

3. Hawk's Heugh: Upper Old Red Sandstone

Round the headland and across the next small bay another high cliff stands above an extensive wave-cut platform. The horizontal red sandstones at the base exhibit numerous bands and patches of bright red nodules. These cornstones are secondary and resulted from caliche soil formation. During evaporation after rare episodes of rainfall, calcium and bicarbonate ions migrated vertically to form a hard surface of carbonate clots. Such calcrete surfaces may be washed

out and redeposited by later desert floods. The red colour is
secondary hematite.

4. Eastern Hole Conglomerate

The top of the Old Red Sandstone facies lies beyond the
next headland; and the basal unit of the Carboniferous is
here taken at the base of the Eastern Hole Conglomerate.
This is a cementstone horizon with conglomeratic layers containing yellow angular clasts of dolomite, together with fish
scales and spines.

5. Sanguinolites band

Overlying the conglomerate is a 25-cm band, not very
clearly seen amongst the pebbles, containing coalified plant
fragments and stems (*Lepidodendron*) and the bivalve
Sanguinolites, with rare ostracods and fish scales. This band
is succeeded by a grey siltstone bed forming a ridge about
2 m high in which excellent climbing ripples are displayed.
The crests of these ripples, migrating eastwards, can be followed through successive layers, testifying to very rapid
deposition of voluminous sediments in a fast-flowing current.
Do not hammer these exposures.

6. Horse Road Sandstone

The pale grey-green Horse Road Sandstone is largely
false-bedded and shows many slump-structures; good
examples of these can be collected in pebbles. The top of this
sandstone forms a small headland at the north end of Eastern
Hole. Very large concretions up to 1·5 m diam. in the
sandstone, are visible in the cliff face, while others have
worked loose and form giant round pebbles. Secondary concretions can be seen within some of the larger concretions. In
the bay beyond, some of the strata above the Horse Road
Sandstone are cut out by the WSW-ENE trending Cove
Fault with a downthrow to the north.

7. Kip Carle Sandstone, Cove Fault

The pale brown medium to coarse grained Kip Carle
Sandstone forms the next prominent high point across the
bay, where it dips very steeply due to the drag effects of the
Cove Fault. The fault can also be seen running from the base

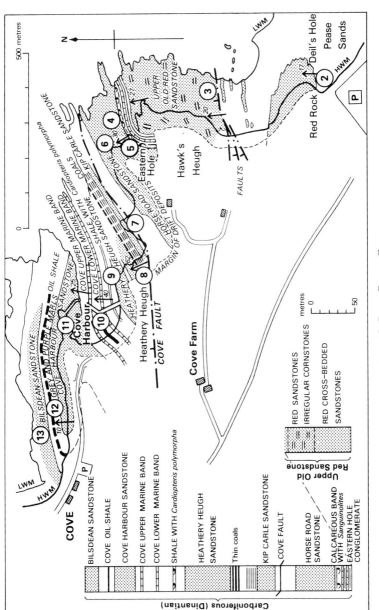

MAP 17. Pease Bay to Cove

of this high point across the next bay, where it forms a marked inclined gully and a fault-breccia in the opposite cliff.

8. Scremerston Coal Group?

Beyond the sandstone the beds are thrown almost vertical by the faulting. A cyclical sequence of thin coals and seatclays separated by sandstones may be equivalent to the Scremerston Coal Group of Northumbria. Below one of the coals is a ganister, a hard white seatrock in which the rootlets of coal-forming plants can be seen.

9. Heathery Heugh Sandstone

The last cliff before Cove Harbour is formed by the red-stained Heathery Heugh Sandstone, through which a narrow gap leads to the harbour. Some of the sandstone is slumped, but the upper part is formed of successive cross-stratified units, well displayed in gullies on the south side of the harbour.

10. Cove Harbour

In the harbour, shales and sandstones dip some 40° to the north. A band containing the excellently preserved seed fern *Cardiopteris polymorpha* (Figure 18) is present but this together with the succeeding Cove Marine Bands is not easily found. With respect to the harbour wall, the Cove Lower Marine Band is the more easily found, outcropping 10 m south of the angle in the harbour wall; the fossils are found in layers through some 2 m of strata. Crinoid ossicles are dominant, whilst other fossils are fragmentary, including sanguinolitid and nuculid bivalves and the brachiopods *Productus redesdalensis*, *Punctospirifer scabricosta*, and *Composita*. The Cove Upper Marine Band can be found at low tide close to the harbour wall. It is about 1 m thick and is mainly shaly with impure limestones; the brachiopod *Punctospirifer scabricosta* is common, as is the bivalve *Aviculopecten*.

A full list of fossils is given by Wilson (1952), including those from nearby inland exposures of the Cove Lower Marine Band. An Asbian (B) age is given by the goniatite *Beyrichoceratoides redesdalensis*.

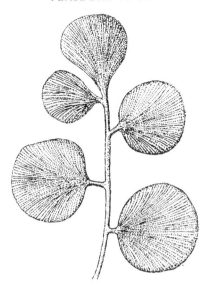

FIG 18. Cardiopteris polymorpha

11. Cove Harbour Sandstone

Ascend the path behind the harbour through the tunnel cut in the Cove Harbour Sandstone, to the village of Cove. The sandstone is purplish-red, yellow in places, false-bedded and rather coarse. There are abundant lenticles of deep-red and buff sandy shale near the base of the upper half. This sandstone marks a temporary return to desert-fluviatite conditions.

12, 13. Cove Oil-Shale and Bilsdean Sandstone

The higher beds north of Cove are not easily accessible, but are well seen from the cliff-top car park at Cove village. In the bay, green and purple marls 6 m thick are overlain by the 30-cm Cove Oil-shale which can be traced westwards for about 500 m, dipping north at 10–15°. The uppermost beds that can be seen, belong to the yellow, fine-grained and evenly bedded Bilsdean Sandstone.

Return to Cockburnspath via Cove or to Pease Bay.

E. N. K. CLARKSON

SICCAR POINT: HUTTON'S CLASSIC UNCONFORMITY

O.S. 1:50000 Sheet 67 Duns and Dunbar
B.G.S. 1:50000 Sheet 34 Eyemouth
Route: Map 18

HISTORICALLY the Siccar Point unconformity is world-famous because its discoverer, James Hutton, was the first geologist to grasp the true significance of such a structure. Although this was not the first unconformity that Hutton had observed—the others were in Arran in 1786 and Jedburgh in 1787—it is certainly the most spectacular. His view of the rocks of the Earth as being the products of an essentially cyclical, oft-repeated process was triumphantly demonstrated at Siccar Point in 1788.

Siccar Point (NT 813 710) lies on the coast 4 km east of Cockburnspath. Turn east off the A1, a little over 2 km south of Cockburnspath on to the A1107. This road crosses the post-glacial gorge of the Pease Burn almost at once and the quarry road to Siccar Point turns off 450 m on the left after the narrow bridge over the gorge. Keep to the right fork of the quarry road, cross the grid bridge and continue along an extremely fine glacial drainage channel into Old Cambus Quarry. Continue through the north-east gate in the quarry and strike obliquely left up the hillside towards the far corner of the field, 60 m below which lies Siccar Point and Hutton's unconformity. From the cliffs a fine panorama can be seen to the north-west of the Upper Old Red Sandstone grading up into the grey sandstones of the Lower Carboniferous (Cove Excursion). The lighthouse in the middle distance at Barns Ness lies on the Lower Limestone Group (Catcraig Excursion) and in the far distance the Bass Rock juts out from the sea with North Berwick Law lying inland slightly to the west. Both are plugs of phonolitic trachyte (North Berwick Excursion).

Siccar Point speaks eloquently for itself and needs little description. It is spectacular at any stage of the tide. An

146

inclined uneven basement of vertical greywackes and shales of Llandovery, Silurian, age youngs to the WNW and is covered unconformably by gently dipping dull-red breccia and sandstone of Upper Devonian or Lower Dinantian age. The breccia is composed of greywacke fragments. The breccia and sandstones were formed under flood conditions. The strong imbricate structure of the clasts in the breccia shows that the direction of derivation of the material was from the NNE and not from the cliffs above.

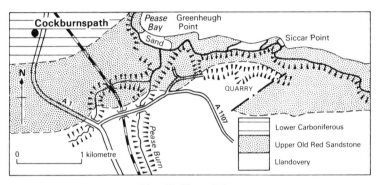

MAP 18. Siccar Point

Both Hutton and Playfair deserve to be quoted. Hutton described it (1795, I, 458) as follows:

"Having taken boat at Dunglass burn, we set out to explore the coast; and, we observed the horizontal sandstone turn up near the Pease burn, rising towards the schistus. We found the junction of that schistus with the red sandstone and marly strata on the shore and sea bank, at St. Helens, corresponding in general with what we had observed in the burns to the westward. But, at Siccar Point, we found a beautiful picture of this junction washed bare by the sea. The sandstone strata are partly washed away, and partly remaining upon the ends of the vertical schistus; and, in many places, points of the schistus strata are seen standing up through among the sandstone, the greatest part of which is worn away. Behind this again we have a natural section of those sandstone strata, containing fragments of the schistus.

After this nothing appears but the schistus rocks, until sandstone and marl again are found at Red-heugh above the vertical strata. From that bay to Fast Castle we had nothing to observe but the schistus, which is continued without interruption to St. Abb's Head. Beyond this, indeed, there appears to be something above the schistus; and great blocks of a red whin-stone or basaltes come down from the height and lie upon the shore; but we could not perceive distinctly how the upper mass is connected with the vertical schistus which is continued below.

Our attention was now directed to what we could observe with respect to the schisti, of which we had most beautiful views and most perfect sections. Here are two objects to be held in view, in making those observations; the original formation or stratification of the schisti, and the posterior operations by which the present state of things has been procured. We had remarkable examples for the illustration of both those subjects (Figure 19).

Fig 19. Siccar Point

With regard to the first, we have every where among the rocks many surfaces of the erected strata laid bare, in being separated. Here we found the most distinct marks of strata of sand modified by moving water. It is no other than that which we every day observe upon the sands of our own shore, when the sea has ebbed and left them in a waved figure, which cannot be mistaken. Such figures as these are extremely common in our sandstone strata; but this is an object which I never had distinctly observed in the alpine schisti; although, considering that the original of those schisti was strata of sand, and formed in water, there was no reason to doubt of such a thing being found. But here the examples are so many and so distinct, that it could not fail to give us great satisfaction.

We were no less gratified in our view with respect to the other object, the mineral operations by which soft strata, regularly formed in horizontal planes at the bottom of the sea had been hardened and displaced. Fig. 4 represents one of those examples; it was drawn by Sir James Hall from a perfect section in the perpendicular cliff at Lumesden burn. Here is not only a fine example of the bendings of the strata, but also of a horizontal shift or hitch of those erected strata."

Hutton's clinical description is in marked contrast to that of the eloquent prose of Playfair (1805, 71–72).

"The ridge of the Lammer-muir Hills in the south of Scotland, consists of primary micaceous schistus, and extends from St Abb's-head westward, till it joins the metalliferous mountains above the source of the Clyde. The sea-coast affords a transverse section of this alpine tract at its eastern extremity, and exhibits the change from the primary to the secondary strata, both on the south and on the north. Dr Hutton wished particularly to examine the latter of these, and on this occasion Sir James Hall and I had the pleasure to accompany him. We sailed in a boat from Dunglass, on a day when the fineness of the weather permitted us to keep close to the foot of the rocks which line the shore in that quarter, directing our course southwards, in search of the termination of the secondary strata. We made a high rocky point or headland, the Siccar, near which, from our observations on the shore, we knew that the object we were in search of was likely to be discovered. On landing at this point, we found that we actually trode on the primeval rock, which forms alternately the base and the summit of the present land. It is here a micaceous schistus, in beds nearly vertical, highly indurated, and stretching from south-east to north-west. The surface of this rock runs with a moderate ascent from the level of low-water, at which we landed, nearly to that of high-water, where the schistus has a thin covering of red horizontal sandstone laid over it; and this sandstone, at the distance of a few yards farther back, rises into a very high perpendicular cliff. Here, therefore, the immediate contact of the two rocks is not only visible, but is curiously dissected and laid open by the action of waves. The rugged tops of the schistus are seen penetrating into the horizontal beds of sandstone, and the lowest of these last form a breccia containing fragments of schistus, some round and others angular, united by an arenaceous cement.

Dr Hutton was highly pleased with appearances that set in so clear a light the different formations of the parts which compose the exterior crust of the earth, and where all the circumstances were combined that could render the observation satisfactory and precise. On us who saw these phenomena for the first time, the impression made will not easily be forgotten. The palpable evidence presented to us, of one of the most extraordinary and important facts in the natural history of the earth, gave a reality and substance to those theoretical speculations, which, however probable, had never till now been directly authenticated by the testimony of the senses. We often said to ourselves, What clearer evidence could we have had of the different formation of these rocks, and of the long interval which separated their formation, had we actually seen them emerging from the bosom the deep? We felt ourselves necessarily carried back to the time when the schistus on which we stood was yet at the bottom of the sea, and when the sandstone before us was only beginning to be deposited in the shape of sand or mud, from the waters of a superincumbent ocean. An epocha still more remote presented itself, when even the most ancient of these rocks instead of standing upright in vertical beds, lay in horizontal planes at the bottom of the sea, and was not yet disturbed by that immeasurable force which has burst asunder the solid pavement of the globe. Revolutions still more remote appeared in the distance of this extraordinary perspective. The mind seemed to grow giddy by looking so far into the abyss of time; and while we listened with earnestness and admiration to the philosopher who was now unfolding to us the order and series of these wonderful events, we became sensible how much farther reason may sometimes go than imagination can venture to follow. As for the rest, we were truly fortunate in the course we had pursued in this excursion; a great number of other curious and important facts presented themselves, and we returned, having collected, in one day, more ample materials for future speculation, than have sometimes resulted from years of diligent and laborious research."

Other localities might seem to be an anticlimax after Siccar Point, but three in the general area are worth mentioning. The first is an anticline of Silurian greywackes and shales exposed in the old quarry (801 653) at Grantshouse, some 5 km south of the junction of the A1107 with the A1. The core of the fold is cut by a minor reversed fault trending parallel to the fold axis and downthrowing to the south-east. Cleavage is developed in the shales and slickensiding seen in bedding planes. Graded bedding, flute marks and groove moulds are among the more common sedimentary structures.

Hutton owned two farms, not one as is commonly recorded, and lived in one of them, Slighhouses (823 593) between 1754 and 1767. This farm can be reached by turning off the A1 some 6 km south-east of Grantshouse on to the B6437 then west on the B6438 for 3 km (822 603) to turn south on an unclassified road. The second is an upland farm, Nether Monynut (728 645), and lies some 4 km north-west of Abbey St Bathans. On a fine day this part of the Border country can be delightful, but if it is wet . . . !

G. Y. CRAIG

LAMMERMUIR DEANS

O.S. 1:50000 Sheet 67 Duns and Dunbar
B.G.S. 1:50000 Sheet 33E Dunbar
Route: Map 19

THIS excursion looks at the Lower Old Red Sandstone conglomerates which fill a large pre-Devonian valley cut across the Lower Palaeozoic greywackes and shales of the Lammermuir Hills, south from Dunbar. Known as the Great Conglomerates they were thought to be Upper Old Red Sandstone in age (Clough *et al.* 1910) but are now believed to be equivalent to the many conglomerates of Lower Old Red Sandstone age found in other parts of the Midland Valley. As well as looking at some of the best exposures in the conglomerates, several unusual weathering phenomena can be seen in the two adjacent deans or narrow valleys. The excursion involves 3 km of rough walking and takes at least 3 hours. It could complement a visit to Siccar Point. The area is a nature reserve managed by the Scottish Wildlife Trust to preserve an unusual calcicolous (lime-loving) flora. The excursion starts at Wester Aikengall (NT 709 708), reached by minor roads from Innerwick or Oldhamstocks. There is reasonable roadside parking.

1. Wester Aikengall: Glacial Channel, Corrom

The cottage is set by a large glacial channel, cut by meltwater flowing from the north and continuing eastwards along the dry valley round Cocklaw Hill to the sea. The Aikengall Water, emerging from a side valley, has built an alluvial fan (called a corrom) which forms a watershed across the glacial channel.

2 and 3. Sheeppath Dean: Conglomerate Gorge

Follow the Aikengall Water westwards where it flows out of the gorge of Sheeppath Dean (2). Gentler slopes of till cap the steep-sided gorge cut in red conglomerate with mostly

152

greywacke cobbles up to 30 cm across. The clasts are largely matrix-supported and commonly show imbrication and parallel orientation, features which suggest they are torrential or flash flood deposits derived from nearby alluvial fans. The sandy matrix contains lime as evidenced by the unusual lime-loving flora, mainly mosses and ferns, which has established itself on the dripping walls of the gorge.

Upstream the gorge narrows to a spectacular slit only a metre or two wide, but over 20 m high, where the stream has eroded along a straight joint. Although the way can be barred by deep pools and branches, at times it is possible to negotiate the slit gorge. *This section is not advised for individuals or large parties.* Continue up the gorge, past a 1·2 m wide vertical basalt dyke oblique to the gorge, to the point below the wood where the valley opens up sufficiently to climb up the south bank by a sheep track (3). Alternatively,

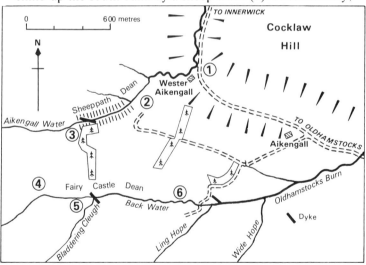

MAP 19. Lammermuir Deans

it is necessary to return downstream before bypassing the slit gorge high up on the south side of the valley. In this case it is worth going down for another look at the gorge upstream at (3). For the next localities proceed south across the ridge keeping to the west side of the wood.

4 and 5. Fairy Castle Dean: Conglomerate, Erosion Features

In contrast to the green pastured till of the Lammermuir ridges, the bare arid red conglomerate valley appears like a canyon from the American West, complete with rock pillars. The valley can be best appreciated by walking along the edge to the viewpoint (4) where the E-W valley turns to the south-west. On descending into the valley the conglomerate is seen to consist of coarse and fine beds with a sandy matrix, and dipping gently to the east-north-east. The cobbles are sub-angular to sub-rounded, generally 5 to 30 cm in size and mostly of Silurian greywackes. Examples can also be found of cobbles derived from felsic dykes, quartz veins, chert, jasper and other lithologies associated with the Silurian greywackes. Fan-shaped screes of cobbles, weathered out from the conglomerate, have formed along the base of the valley sides, mimicking the conditions under which the conglomerate originally formed, in alluvial fans at the foot of rugged mountains. Near Fairy Castle (5), at the confluence with Bladdering Cleugh, a vertical basalt dyke, almost a metre wide and trending NW-SE, has been intruded into and baked the conglomerate. Note the jointing on the dyke and the manner in which the baked conglomerate stands up, resistant to erosion.

6. Back Water: Alluvium

Continue downstream along the usually dried up alluvial flat of the Back Water, a headstream of the Oldhamstocks Burn. The alluvium is a gravel formed of cobbles from the conglomerate, the cobbles becoming more rounded from each successive cycle of erosion. Return by the track to Easter Aikengall Farm, and by the road back to the starting point.

A. D. McAdam

4. The Great Conglomerate, with recent scree fans. Fairy Castle Dean

RIVER NORTH ESK

O.S. 1:50000 Sheet 66 Edinburgh
B.G.S. 1:50000 Sheet 32E Edinburgh (Solid)
B.G.S. 1:63360 Sheet 32 Edinburgh (Drift)
Route: Map 20

AT the end of the last ice age, torrential meltwater from a decaying ice-sheet lying between the Moorfoot Hills and the Pentland Hills, cut deep gorges through glacial deposits and into the underlying rocks as it rushed to the sea. The gorge of the River North Esk between Polton and Roslin cuts deep into the Passage Group rocks known locally as the Roslin Sandstone, and further upstream there are fine exposures in the sandstones of the Upper Limestone Group and the Roslin Sandstone (Tulloch and Walton 1958, pp. 61–92).

The whole excursion, along the River North Esk from Polton to Penicuik, makes a good day, or it can be split into two half day excursions, with Roslin as the mid-point. Rights of way beside the river exist for the whole length of the excursion. Lowland and Eastern Scottish buses serve Polton, Roslin and Penicuik.

1. Polton Bridge: Landslide, Glacial Deposits

The northern part of the excursion starts from the north side of the river by Polton Bridge (NT 288 648). The path on the west bank skirts the head scarp of the huge landslide of 1979 (Baird and Smellie, 1980). The top part of the landslide is sand and gravel in which several rock types, including andesites and basalts, can be recognised as originating from the Pentland Hills. The bottom third of the slope is boulder clay.

2. Maiden Castle: Meander, Earthwork

Passing the landslide, a detour can be made over the narrow neck of land into the loop of the North Esk known as the Maiden Castle. This barely discernible earthwork is the

155

remains of a Bronze or Iron Age defended area. Cliffs at the far side of the meander show basal posts of red Roslin Sandstone overlying yellow bedded sandstones and grey or purple mudstones. The route continues south through a fairly open valley with over-steepened sides.

3. Hawthornden Castle: Gorge in Roslin Sandstone

Upstream, south-west from Hawthornden Castle, once the home of the poet Drummond (Macgibbon and Ross 1887), the North Esk runs through a 1·5 km long gorge. From a point about 100 m downstream of Hawthornden Castle, it is possible to leave the path when the water is low and wade up the gorge, but once this route is commenced one must continue to the end of the gorge or return to the starting point. Should one venture by this way, then from the riverside just 100 m upstream from Hawthornden Castle can be seen the highest cliff section in the whole excursion. Sheer cliffs of a beautiful rose-red sandstone rise abruptly from the north bank of the river to a height of 30 m, stretching for over 100 m along the gorge. Massive posts of sandstone in this section show very fine examples of current-bedding. Along the bottom of the gorge the river has scoured out the softest parts of the bedrock to form pot holes, undercuts and deep narrow channels.

Alternatively, superb geological and historical views of Hawthornden Castle can be seen from the cliff top high on the west bank of the river. By following the path which gently descends to just above the river, beautiful exposures of the pinkish red Roslin Sandstone can be seen. Current-bedding, apparent everywhere, often on a large scale, shows that this sandstone was laid down in a high energy, continually changing river environment. Bands of pebbles at the base of this pebbly, gritty sandstone indicate each surge of current.

4 and 5. Roslin Gorge: Roslin Sandstone, Tufa

Towards Wallace's cave below Gorton House (4), the gorge becomes narrower and even more spectacular. Note how cliffs undercut by each river meander alternate along the valley with steep wooded slopes of slipped rock and glacial deposits. High on the west side of the gorge, 100 m downstream

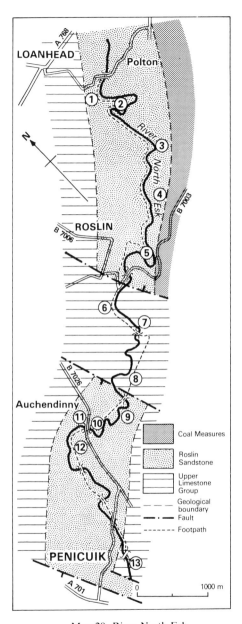

MAP 20. River North Esk

of a sandstone sluice, a small area of calcareous tufa lies on the Roslin Sandstone. This unusual deposit, of uncertain source and age, can be attributed to a supersaturated stream of lime-rich water. Just beyond the tufa, is the first of several streams which plunge in cascades down the cliff face from the hanging valleys above. Upstream one emerges from the gorge below the towering walls of Roslin Castle (5), home of the Sinclair family since the 14th Century (Macgibbon and Ross 1887). A fault throws down the Roslin Sandstone seen in the gorge against Upper Limestone Group strata to the south.

6. Old Roslin Powder Mill: Decalcified Sandstone

The southern part of the excursion starts at the gates of the Old Roslin Powder Mill, the area surrounding which is a country park supervised by Midlothian District Council. The gates are at the sharp bend on the B7003 below Roslin village (273 633). On the right of the track through the Old Powder Mill are several embayments cut into the sandstone to provide secure and separate sites for the various buildings connected with the manufacture of gunpowder. In the walls of many of these embayments considerable decalcification of the sandstone has taken place, possibly due to acid water from peat banks on the high ground beyond running down the steep faces (Sinclair 1794). The basal portion of these sandstones contains fragments of the underlying mudstone, bands of small pebbles and, in several places, plant fossils such as *Calamites*.

7. Hare Craig: Upper Limestone Group

The track crosses the North Esk on a wooden bridge (266 621) from which can be seen a superb section of Upper Limestone Group sediments on the east bank of the river. Upwards from river level are several cycles of sandstone and mudstone overlain by a fireclay some 3 m thick. Massive sandstones have channelled into the top of the fireclay and continue upwards for 10 m to the viewpoint of Hare Craig on top of the cliff. Leaving the river just beyond the bridge, the path goes up the steep slope of the south bank to join the track of the old Eskbank to Penicuik railway which forms the rest of the route to Penicuik.

8. *Hare Craig to Firth Viaduct: Castlecary Limestone, Roslin Sandstone*

A scramble down the ditch (261 617) will reveal a small exposure of a fine-grained grey limestone which occurs 15 m above the sharp bend in the river. Mineralogically this is a dolomitic limestone, suggesting correlation with the Castlecary Limestone. The beds seen downriver are therefore high in the Upper Limestone Group. Returning to the track, the journey continues along a more open stretch of the North Esk Valley with the river sweeping to the right. Just downstream from the Firth Viaduct, a fault brings a return to the Roslin Sandstone which continues all the way to Penicuik. This sandstone, however, lacks the coarseness, current-bedding and colour of the Roslin Sandstone at the type locality downstream from Roslin Castle. The rocks around Auchendinny either exhibit lateral changes in sedimentation, or lie at different stratigraphic horizons.

9. *Firth House: Sandstone, Artificial Tufa*

When the water is low, and one is clad in wellington boots, it is possible to leave the track of the railway at the Firth Viaduct, descend to the riverside and follow the river bank around the two spurs opposite Firth House. About 100 m downstream from the waterfall formed by a small stream on the south bank between Auchendinny House and Firth House, well-defined current bedding can be seen on the massive bottom post of two major sandstone ribs exposed high on the cliffs of the south bank. Only 25 m upstream from the waterfall, 15 m of the river margin are covered in a calcareous tufa deposited by water seeping from further up the bank. This tufa, although appearing similar to naturally occurring tufa, has been deposited as a secondary mineral by water perculating through the caustic dump of the Dalmore Paper Mill—an interesting example of a geological feature resulting from man's activities.

10 and 11. *Dalmore Mill: Roslin Sandstone*

Rejoin the track just downriver from the Dalmore Mill (10), pass through the tunnel under the B7026 and cross to the west bank of the North Esk by the old railway bridge which starts just beyond the tunnel. On the opposite side of the river, poorly exposed sandstone with almost horizontal bedding can be seen (11). Beyond, sandstones with a westward dip of 15° gradually become horizontal further upstream. In a rapidly eroding bank 6 m high, one can see an exposure of sandstones and mudstones which have almost certainly slumped from further up the bank.

12. Glencorse Barracks: Sandstone Quarry

Opposite Glencorse Barracks sewage works, an old quarry exposes some 6 m of pale creamy buff sandstone, in places stained with iron. Within the horizontal beds, posts of sandstone up to 45 cm thick are separated by thin mudstone bands.

From the old quarry to Penicuik, a distance of 1 km, the valley opens out and takes on a more mature aspect. This appearance, however, is deceptive as the slopes up to the surrounding farmland are steep and liable to landslide under adverse conditions.

13. Penicuik: Calmy Limestone

Continue beyond the Penicuik sewage works, across the bridge at Harper's Brae (245 605) and take the walkway upstream on the east bank of the river to a point 60 m upstream from the wooden walkway bridge. Exposed just at water level on the east bank, is a limestone correlated with the Calmy Limestone. Return to the bridge at Harper's Brae and take the Kirkhill Road which rises steeply into Penicuik.

W. BAIRD

PENTLAND HILLS

O.S. 1:50000 Sheet 66 Edinburgh
B.G.S. 1:50000 Sheets 32W Livingstone, 32E Edinburgh
Route: Maps 21 and 22

THE Pentland Hills are made up of Lower Old Red
Sandstone lavas and sediments with a core of Silurian rocks.
The latter are generally steeply dipping and are exposed in
three inliers known as the North Esk Inlier (p. 174), the
Bavelaw Castle Inlier and the Loganlee-Craigenterrie Inlier.
The Lower Old Red Sandstone lavas consists of ten groups of
lava flows (Mykura 1960, pp. 131–155) which include olivine-
basalts, andesites, trachytes, dacites and rhyolites, as well as
acid and basic tuffs. They attain a thickness of over 2000 m in
the north, but thin rapidly to the south. Near the southern
end of their outcrop up to 600 m of Lower Old Red Sandstone conglomerate and grit are present between the lavas
and the underlying Silurian strata. Upper Old Red
Sandstone, composed mainly of pink sandstone, rests unconformably on an eroded and undulating land surface of the
older rocks. It forms the East and West Cairn Hills in the
south-western part of the range but near the northern end of
the Pentlands, at Torphin Hill, it is very thin and in places
completely overlapped by basal Carboniferous beds.

The present topographic pattern of the Pentland Hills was
initiated in the Tertiary era, and was later modified by the
Highland ice which overwhelmed the area in Pleistocene
times. Thus some of the Pentland passes, such as the
Cauldstane Slap and the Bore Stane, are sited on the be-
headed courses of Tertiary rivers which drained to the south-
east, while other major through-routes were formed as late-
glacial drainage channels carrying meltwaters from the
north-west slopes of the range into the Midlothian Basin.

The itinerary forms the basis for two half-day excursions
from Edinburgh.

161

Excursion A—Bavelaw Castle to Loganlee Reservoir
(Route: Map 21)

The object of this excursion is to study the Silurian rocks of the Bavelaw Castle and Loganlee inliers, the overlying conglomerate, felsite and basic lavas of Lower Old Red Sandstone age, as well as the red sandstones ascribed to the Upper Old Red Sandstone which rest unconformably on all the older rocks. In addition, the route follows one of the major glacial melt-water channels in the Pentland Hills.

Access can be either by private transport or Eastern Scottish service bus. Using a car or private bus, travel to Balerno and thence south past Marchbank Hotel to a small car park (NT 165 637). From there the route stays close to the public right-of-way past Bavelaw Castle to the head of Loganlee Reservoir and returns the same way. Total walking distance is 10 km; time 3 hours. Alternatively, take the service bus to Balerno and then walk 4 km to Bavelaw Castle. The homeward journey can also be made by walking down the valley of the Logan Burn past Glencorse Reservoir to Flotterstone, and thence by service bus to Edinburgh. The total walking distance is 15 km, and a time of at least 4½ hours should be allowed.

1. Bavelaw Castle: Late-Glacial Drainage Channels

A traverse from the road-end at Bavelaw Castle to the wall on the north-west slope of Hare Hill (168 623), 600 m to the south, crosses the intakes of three late-glacial drainage channels which carried melt-waters from the decaying ice just west of Hare Hill via Green Cleugh to Loganlee. The courses of the two higher channels are successively truncated by those of the lower ones.

Locality 1 forms a good viewpoint from which the following features can be observed:

(a) Two small curved drainage channels contouring the low ground immediately to the south.

(b) The profile of the north slope of Hare Hill, originally an evenly sloping hillside, in which the Bavelaw-Loganlee channel is now entrenched.

(c) The alluvial flat extending for 1·2 km west-south-westwards from Threipmuir Reservoir, which may have

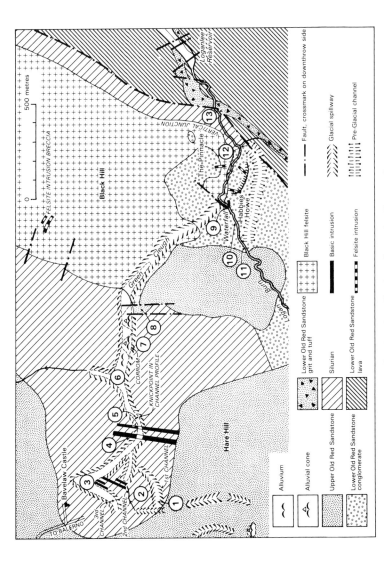

MAP 21. Bavelaw Castle to Loganlee Reservoir

been part of the floor of an ice-dammed lake formed at a later stage in the retreat of the ice-sheet. The waters from this lake escaped through the gap between Black Hill and Bell's Hill (198 643) to join the lower part of the Bavelaw-Loganlee channel which flowed by Glencorse Reservoir to Flotterstone.

(d) The flat top of East Cairn Hill (560 m) which is thought to be a residual portion of the Tertiary 600 m peneplain.

Features of interest seen looking west from here are (left to right): Corston Hill (095 635), composed of mugearite and olivine-basalt lavas of basal Oil-Shale Group (Arthur's Seat Volcanic Rocks) age; Dalmahoy Hill (135 779), a sill of teschenitic dolerite containing the rare mineral chlorophaeite; and Ratho Hill (128 714), a sill of quartz-dolerite.

2 and 3. Bavelaw Castle: Silurian

Silurian rocks of the Bavelaw Castle inlier are exposed in two small quarries south and west of Bavelaw Castle. The strata are nearly vertical and consist of grey-green mudstones with silty laminae. They are poorly fossiliferous but some of the genera recorded are: the brachiopods *Lissatrypa* and *Lingula*, the trilobites *Leonaspis lothiana* and *Acernaspis* sp, the gastropod (?)*Liospira*, bivalves, (?)*Ctenodonta* and orthocone cephalopods.

The beds of the Bavelaw Castle inlier were for a long time thought to be of Wenlock age, but Lamont (1947) has shown that they are of Upper Llandovery age and may belong to the oldest Silurian rocks exposed in the Pentland Hills. In both the quarries the sediments are intruded by dykes of fine-grained andesine-dolerite. There are five dykes varying in thickness from 0·9 m to 3·4 m in the northern quarry and two, respectively 1 m and 7·5 m thick, in the southern. Most of the dykes are slightly transgressive to the bedding of the sediments.

4. North of Hare Hill: Dykes

A large swarm of highly decomposed basic dykes is exposed on the slopes of the glacial melt-water channel between 500 m and 550 m south-east of Bavelaw Castle. The most westerly of these dykes may be up to 45 m thick and all are so highly decomposed that they are easily mistaken for grit.

5 and 6. North of Hare Hill: Glacial Melt-water Channels

The gentle gradient of the floor of the channel remains constant as far as a point 600 m south-east of Bavelaw Castle (5). Beyond this point it steepens slightly and the valley floor loses some of the characteristic flatness of a drainage channel.

The north bank of the original east-west channel is breached 750 m south-east of Bavelaw Castle (6), and a secondary channel leads off northwards. This branch channel has the shape of a typical glacial drainage channel for the first 130 m of its course, but beyond this it deteriorates into a normal stream valley. It appears to have been initiated during a late stage in the decay of the ice-sheet that covered the north-west slope of the Pentland Hills. At first the ice in this area formed a continuous sheet and the only escape for the glacial meltwater was eastward, probably in a tunnel beneath the ice or along a crevasse in the ice, via the valley of the Logan Burn into the North Esk valley, which had become ice-free by then. As the climate became progressively warmer the local ice would become thinner and the crevasses would widen. The meltwater would eventually find a way along one of these crevasses and flow directly downhill towards the valley now occupied by Threipmuir Reservoir. Eventually all the meltwater would pass through this more steeply inclined northern channel. This led to the down-cutting of the floor of the original channel on either side of the new outlet, the limit of back-cutting being marked by knick-points.

Up to 400 m farther east several small streamlets, which have cut gullies into the north slope of Hare Hill, have deposited small alluvial cones on the flat bottom of the main channel. One of these now forms the watershed in the channel and is thus an example of a delta-watershed or corrom.

7 and 8. North-east of Hare Hill: Silurian, Old Red Sandstone and Felsite

The westerly of the two big gullies (7) cut in the south bank of the channel exposes sparsely fossilferous, steeply inclined Silurian strata, which consist of purplish-grey siltstones and mudstones with thin ochre-coloured flaggy ribs. The fossils recorded from this locality include: *Lingula*, the graptolites *Monograptus* and *Retiolites*, the problematic organism *Dictyocaris*, rare bivalves and orthocone cephalopods.

The western bank of the second gully (8) shows Silurian strata which dip steeply to the west-south-west and have yielded the trilobite *Leonaspis*, brachiopods such as *Lissatrypa*, bivalves and orthocone cephalopods. The east bank of this gully is cut in Upper Old Red Sandstone, which consists of pink sandstone with layers full of small sub-angular pebbles of quartzite and Pentland lavas. The sandstone has been faulted down against the Silurian to the west. For a short distance east of the gully, Upper Old Red Sandstone appears to rest directly on Silurian, but about 30 m east of the small sandstone cliff an exposure in a small water-scoop shows Upper Old Red Sandstone resting on weathered felsite.

Felsite is exposed for a considerable distance on both sides of Green Cleugh, and the accumulation of its platy scree has here obliterated the original cross-section of the glacial drainage channel. The felsite, which forms Black Hill, has in thin-section the characteristics of microgranite, and is a distinctive rock as it contains porphyritic crystals of micropegmatite, a graphic intergrowth of quartz and feldspar. Near Habbies Howe the felsite on the south slope of Black Hill is unconformably overlain by a thin cap of Lower Old Red Sandstone conglomerate which dips at up to 25° to the south-south-west.

9–11. Logan Water: Lower Old Red Sandstone Conglomerate, Glacial Features

Lower Old Red Sandstone conglomerate is well exposed in the gorge of the Logan Water between localities 9 and 11. It is a fluvial conglomerate with rounded pebbles of greywacke, jasperised basic lava and radiolarian chert, which were probably derived from the south. Blocks of Silurian limestone which have yielded corals and other fossils, are found 90 m to 140 m upstream from the lowest waterfall (10). Near the waterfall the conglomerate passes down into a brownish pebbly grit which contains, in addition to the rounded pebbles mentioned above, some smaller angular pebbles of igneous rocks. The latter are mainly trachytes and more basic lavas, but a number are composed of felsite containing phenocrysts identical to those in the Black Hill felsite. Such felsitic fragments are well seen in some loose blocks of conglomerate lying just east of the stream at the point where it emerges from its gorge on to the flat bottom of the glacial drainage channel. The conglomerate, both in the gorge and in the cliff to the east, is cut by irregular sills and dykes of Black Hill felsite and there is also a sill of andesine-dolerite which crosses the lowest waterfall.

There is a marked change in the character of the valley of the Logan Burn at a point 250 m upstream from the waterfall (11). Above this, the stream flows in a fairly wide valley which is largely floored by boulder clay: below, it passes into a post-glacial rock gorge. The pre-glacial course of the Logan Burn appears to run to the south of Habbies Howe cliff to join the present course of the stream about 400 m south-west of Loganlee.

12. South-west of Loganlee Reservoir: Black Hill Felsite and Silurian

The vertical junction between the Black Hill felsite and the Silurian strata of the Loganlee-Craigenterrie inlier is exposed just north of the path 450 m south-west of Loganlee Reservoir. Slightly higher up the hillside the felsite is said to spread out horizontally in places over the truncated edges of the Silurian sediments, but the evidence for this cannot be conclusively demonstrated from present-day exposures. Steeply inclined Silurian strata are exposed on the track for a distance of 200 m down the valley. They consist of grey shales and mudstones and have in the past yielded several species of graptolites. Thin beds of fine-grained turbidite sandstone with load and flute casts on their bottom surfaces can be seen. The bottom structures indicate that the beds young to the west-north-west.

The shape and origin of the Black Hill felsite mass has been a matter for some speculation. Geikie suggested that the felsite forms a vertical sheet intruded along the bedding of the Silurian strata, while Peach described it as a laccolith intruded along the plane of unconformity between the Silurian and Old Red Sandstone sediments. More recently it was realised that angular blocks of felsite occur near the base of the overlying conglomerate, that the felsite on the north-west side of Black Hill is locally vesicular, and that certain dyke-like bodies of felsite intrusion-breccia with a markedly scoriaceous matrix occur within the outcrop. A theory which could satisfactorily explain all the observed field relation-ships, is that the felsite may have been extruded in early Old Red Sandstone times to form a cumulo-dome, or mamelon, on the Silurian land surface. This dome was soon covered by greywacke-gravel in which some of the felsite scree forming around the base of the dome was incorporated. The sills and dykes of felsite found in the Lower Old Red Sandstone con-glomerate overlying the felsite are attributed to a later intru-sive phase of activity of the felsite magma.

13. Loganlee: Old Red Sandstone Lavas

The Silurian inlier of Loganlee is bounded on the east by a fault with a large easterly downthrow. This is exposed on the north bank of the stream 240 m south-west of Loganlee Reservoir, where a layer of purple basaltic tuff, intercalated with lavas of the Carnethy group, abuts against the Silurian.

Along the road to Glencorse Reservoir numerous ex-posures of this tuff, locally interbedded with tuffaceous sandstone, and of the Carnethy basalt and basic andesite lavas can be examined. A good section of these rocks, includ-ing some porphyritic flows of basalt, is also exposed in a southern tributary which enters the Logan Burn at Lovers' Loup, 500 m south-west of Loganlee Reservoir.

If this excursion is combined with the Torphin Quarry-Bonaly Tower excursion (p. 169), the path leading from Glencorse Reservoir to Bonaly Tower should be taken. It is then most convenient to reverse the order of localities in the latter itinerary. Alternatively, good exposures in the rhyolite of Bell's Hill and Castlelaw Hill and the biotite-dacite of Capelaw Hill, are easily accessible from Glencorse Reser-voir. Sections of auto-brecciated olivine-basalt flows of the Carnethy Group are exposed along the road to Flotterstone.

Excursion B—Torphin Quarry-White Hill-Bonaly Tower (Route: Map 22)

The excursion is concerned with the Lower Old Red Sandstone basalt, andesite and trachyte lavas and intercalated sedimentary rocks which form the Pentland Hills. It also provides an opportunity to collect a number of vein minerals, particularly baryte.

Access is by Lothian Region Transport bus to Torphin Golf Club, and then 500 m walk to Torphin Quarry. Cars and private buses can be taken to the quarry entrance, where parking space is available. It is advisable to get permission from the quarry operators to enter Torphin Quarry. At the time of writing the faces in the working quarry are loose and dangerous, and special care should be taken at all times. Walking distance is 6 km; time 3 hours.

1. Torphin: Conglomerates

The road to Torphin Quarry passes to the north of a grassed escarpment with poor exposures of pink calcareous conglomerates containing sub-angular pebbles of various Pentland lavas, as well as quartz and quartzite. The age of this conglomerate has been taken as Upper Old Red Sandstone, but a temporary exposure 360 m to the south-east has shown that typical Lower Carboniferous sediments occur very close to the post-Lower Old Red Sandstone unconformity in this area. It is therefore quite likely that the conglomerate is of Lower Carboniferous age, and that the lavas of Torphin Hill and White Hill may have formed an 'island' above the plain of deposition until well into Carboniferous times.

2. Torphin Quarries: Basalt Lavas, Boles, Baryte Veins

The lavas of Torphin Quarries form part of the Warklaw Hill group of olivine-basalts. This is the lowest group in the known portion of the Pentland Hills succession and can itself be divided into four distinctive groups of flows (a–d, of route-map). The basalts exposed in the quarry belong mainly to group b, with some flows of group c near the top of the south-east face.

The basalts of group b are black and fine-grained, with small reddish phenocrysts of olivine pseudomorphed by iron oxide and iddingsite. In thin-section their groundmass contains much alkaline feldspar and they have a trachytic texture. The characteristic feature of the group is the thickness of its two lowest flows. The lowest, which rests on a band of tuff, is up to 18 m thick and is locally flow-brecciated near its top. The second flow which is the flow principally worked in the quarry, attains a thickness of nearly 30 m and is non-vesicular throughout. It is overlain by a prominent bed

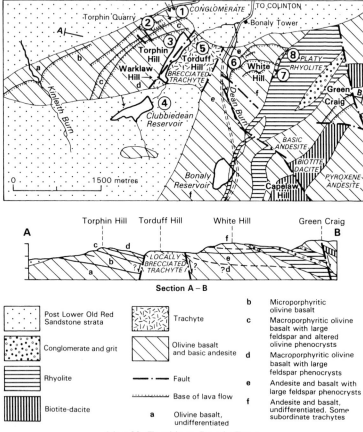

MAP 22. Torphin to Bonaly Tower

of waterlain tuff, composed largely of small rounded clasts of
weathered basalt. The higher lava flows, seen in the upper
face of the quarry, are much thinner and have weathered
tops which pass upward into pebble-beds of weathered lava
debris. This suggests that these flows were undergoing rapid
weathering and some active erosion shortly after their formation. The flows of group c, which are best examined near the
summit of Warklaw Hill, are highly vesicular and are composed of macroporphyritic basalt with phenocrysts of altered
olivine and feldspar in roughly equal numbers. Note: part of
the northern quarry is now filled in, and the lower part of the
original section is no longer exposed.

The faces of Torphin Quarry are cut by a number of small
faults and joints. Some of these are lined with coarsely crystalline baryte and calcite. Good specimens of platy baryte,
including cockscombe spar are to be found. Many lava blocks
lying in the quarry are highly amygdaloidal and some
amygdales contain chalcedony and agate.

3. Torduff Reservoir: Basalt Lavas of Lower Old Red Sandstone, Glacial Features

The highest flows of the Warklaw group (group d) are well
exposed on the roadside on the west bank of Torduff Reservoir. They are usually 3 to 4 m thick and highly amygdaloidal
throughout. The purplish-grey basalts are macro-porphyritic,
with phenocrysts of altered feldspar measuring up to 5 mm
predominating over the smaller altered ferro-magnesian
phenocrysts. In the road-cutting 45 m west of the waterman's
cottage a number of veins and irregular masses of siltstone
and mudstone are found near the top of a flow; these appear
to be filling cracks and cavities in the lava.

Torduff Reservoir lies in the valley formed by a north-east
trending fault. In late glacial times this valley formed part of
a drainage channel which was cut during the final stage in the
northward retreat of the ice-sheet from the Pentland Hills.

4. Clubbiedean Reservoir: Upper Old Red Sandstone Sediments

The unconformity between Lower and Upper Old Red
Sandstone lies close to the south end of Torphin Reservoir.
Sections of Upper Old Red Sandstone are seen in the burn

between the two reservoirs and also close to the road. The sandstone contains a number of thin cornstone (caliche) horizons, which represent fossil soils (pedocals) developed during long periods of reduced deposition in a tropical climate. Outcrops of cornstone occur on the hillside southeast of the track, but the area is fenced off from the public.

5. Torduff Hill: Trachyte Lava of Lower Old Red Sandstone

Torduff Hill is formed of pale-grey fine-grained trachyte, which closely resembles the trachyte of the Braid Hills near Edinburgh. It is locally flow-banded and there are a number of well-defined belts which have been brecciated in a manner suggesting flow-brecciation. The field evidence suggests that this trachyte is separated from the lava groups on either side by faults, and it seems likely, though not certain, that Torduff Hill forms a structural horst.

6. White Hill: Basalt and Andesite of Lower Old Red Sandstone

The lavas forming the crags of White Hill belong to the Bonaly group, which consists of feldspar-phyric olivine-basalts and pyroxene-andesites in its lower part, and of non-porphyritic andesites with one thin flow of trachyte in its upper part. The lower olivine-basalts and andesites are well exposed in the Dean Burn. The upper non-porphyritic flows are seen on White Hill, where they form prominent trap-features, slightly modified by glacial scour.

7 and 8. White Hill Plantation: Rhyolite and Conglomerate of Lower Old Red Sandstone

The Bonaly basalts are overlain by the rhyolites of the Bell's Hill and Howden Burn group. On the north-east slope of White Hill a thin conglomerate with pebbles of greywacke, chert and some basic lavas separates these two groups (7). This conglomerate, as well as the overlying rhyolite, can be traced by several outcrops north-eastwards downhill through White Hill plantation (8). It can here be demonstrated that the conglomerate rests on the truncated edges of the higher flows of the Bonaly group. It is not suggested that a period of earth movement intervened between the eruption of the andesites and the overlying rhyolite: a period of erosion with steep valleys cut into the latest lava flows can be the cause of an angular unconformity of this type.

Return by Bonaly Castle to Colinton.

W. MYKURA

NORTH ESK INLIER

O.S. 1:50000 Sheet 65 Falkirk and West Lothian
B.G.S. 1:50000 Sheet 32W Livingston
Route: Map 23

SILURIAN rocks outcrop in three inliers in the Pentland Hills. The largest of these, the North Esk Inlier, forms the subject of this excursion. The others are the Bavelaw Castle and Loganlea-Craigenterrie inliers (p. 162). Silurian strata in the inliers are generally vertical though rarely gently inclined. They strike SW-NE, young NW and are overlain with angular unconformity by gently dipping Lower Old Red Sandstone greywacke conglomerates. Silurian fossils were first recorded from the Pentlands by McLaren in 1838. Since then local geologists have collected extensively from the inliers, the most prominent being Hardie and Henderson, whose large collections made last century are in the Royal Museum of Scotland. Originally the sediments were thought to be of Wenlock to Downtonian age (Peach & Horne, 1899). However, in an extensive reinvestigation of the fauna, Lamont (1947) determined ages ranging from Upper Llandovery, probably *crenulata* biozone, to Wenlock for the North Esk Group as exposed in the North Esk Inlier. These ages were incorporated in the third survey by the Geological Survey (Mykura & Smith *in* Mitchell & Mykura 1962) and are generally accepted by later workers.

The succession as given by Tipper (1976) and Robertson (in prep.) is as follows, with the localities to be visited numbered:

North Esk Group	metres
Henshaw Formation (? Wenlock) (16–17, 26–29)	
Red conglomerates, cross-bedded micaceous sandstones, olive green shales with one or two bands of fish fragments	730
Wether Law Linn Formation (Llandovery) (11–15, 25, 30)	
Well-laminated brown siltstones with shelly fauna	125
Poorly stratified brown sandy siltstones	45

174

	metres
Wether Law Linn Formation (continued) Highly fossiliferous laminated and bioturbated yellow-brown silty mudstones	40
Cock Rig Formation (Llandovery) (10) Cross stratified red-brown conglomerates and sandstones	80
Deerhope Formation (Llandovery) (6–9) Fossiliferous blue-grey micaceous siltstones and mudstones	250
Reservoir Formation (Llandovery) (1–5, 18–24) Interbedded greenish sandy siltstones and mudstones	1400

The sequence represents a rapid regression from an offshore submarine fan environment (Reservoir Formation, Deerhope Formation and Cock Rig Formation) through a shallow shelf environment in which an abundant and diverse fauna existed, though changing through time (Wether Law Linn Formation) to a terrestrial environment (Henshaw Formation). The most recent bibliography of works on the fossils of the Pentland Hills is given by Clarkson & Howells (1981).

Carlops and West Linton can both be reached by Eastern Scottish service buses. For access to the eastern part of the inlier (Excursions A and B) coaches should be left in Carlops and the 3 km walk taken either by the east bank of the River North Esk or by the farm track to Fairliehope and to the cottage at the reservoir. Private cars may be parked near the cottage. The western end of the inlier (Excursion C) can be reached from West Linton by following the road to Baddinsgill Reservoir where a public car park is provided 1 km from the reservoir. The itinerary forms the basis for one day and two half-day excursions.

Excursion A—River North Esk

The object of this excursion is to study the complete stratigraphy of the Silurian rocks in the North Esk Inlier. The starting point is at the south-west end of the North Esk Reservoir, the total walking distance is approximately 8 to 10 km and the excursion should occupy at least five hours.

1 and 2. River North Esk: Unconformity, Reservoir Formation—Lower

By following the footpath along the River North Esk it is possible to see the Lower Old Red Sandstone strata overlying the inlier. Red conglomerates containing dominantly greywacke cobbles are interbedded with pyroxene andesites of the Carnethy group (Mykura, 1960) and are cut by minor sub-basic intrusions. The position of the unconformity (1) between gently south-east dipping Old Red Sandstone and vertical Silurian strata crosses the river 450 m SSE of the cottage but is not exposed. To the north lie the oldest Silurian sediments to be exposed in the inlier, grey-green muddy siltstones.

Upstream from the unconformity, a gorge (2) cut out by the old overflow channel from the North Esk Reservoir exposes the lower part of the Reservoir Formation. The interbedded siltstones fine sandstones and laminated shales are folded by recumbent sub-isoclinal F_1 folds. Two stages of folding are present in the inlier, this (the older) is only evident in the Reservoir Formation sediments.

3, 4 and 5. North Esk Reservoir: Reservoir Formation—Upper

The east bank of the reservoir (3) provides an excellent and almost complete exposure through 250 m of grey-green and red Reservoir Formation sediments. In the south-east corner of the reservoir are exposed greenish-grey and yellow-brown sandstones and siltstones, finely laminated and forming discrete beds 1 cm to 1 m thick, normally with distinct upper and lower contacts. Internal structures in these show fining-up sequences from massive, relatively coarse bases, through ripple and convolute lamination, occasionally to bioturbated tops. Sedimentary structures indicate palaeocurrents flowing from the east. Rounded mud clasts and the enigmatic fossil *Dictyocaris* are common here in the siltstones but the beds are otherwise unfossiliferous. Some 50 m north of the south-east corner of the reservoir there is a somewhat disturbed zone following which the beds abruptly change to a fine red mudstone, devoid of fossils, but with occasional sandstone bands in its upper part, extending beyond the north-east corner.

The sediments are folded by an open F_2 (kink) fold, only recognised by subtle changes in the strike of the strata. Fold closures show slickensiding and beds are badly fractured; these are not associated with displacement and there seems

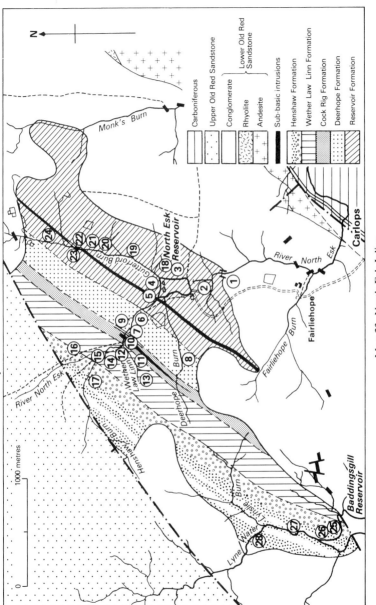

MAP 23. North Esk Inlier

no evidence for major faulting as suggested in the past
(Mykura & Smith, 1962).

The north bank of the reservoir (4) provides an excellent
section through higher sediments in the Reservoir Formation. At the eastern end of this large outcrop is exposed an F_1
fold closure, plunging south-west similar to folds at (2).
Faults trending 150° cut the strata, all with downthrows to
the east of up to 3·5 m.

In the north-west corner of the reservoir (5) the Fairliehope-Gutterford igneous intrusion is exposed. This 2–4 m
thick intrusion is folded by both F_1 and F_2 folds, is only seen
below the Silurian-Old Red Sandstone unconformity, and
must be pre Old Red Sandstone in age. The rock is a highly
altered (chloritised) sub-basic diorite. Intruded sediments
show baked contacts. Above the intrusions, in predominantly fine-grained sediments, rare smooth-shelled
brachiopods (*Lissatrypa atheroidea*) occur.

6 and 7. River North Esk: Deerhope Formation—
Lower

The Deerhope Formation overlies the Reservoir Formation. The top of the Reservoir Formation is marked by the
last thick siltstone unit showing internal structures, and this
bed is exposed in the River North Esk (6). On the hillside to
the east above the contact, fine grey-brown laminated shales,
typical of the Deerhope Formation, show the first elements
of a poor shelly fauna.

Upstream, in patchy exposures, this fauna and flora of
algae, corals, crinoids, brachiopods, bivalves, gastropods,
nautiloids and trilobites becomes common. A large cutting in
the east bank (7), in red shales, is particularly fossiliferous.

8. Deerhope Burn: Deerhope Formation, Deerhope
Coral Bed

Better exposures of the formation are found at the type
locality along the lower reaches of the Deerhope Burn. The
Deerhope Formation is predominantly green and purple
shales containing, in some places, a rich shelly fauna. Interbedded are thin siltstone horizons, in which the fauna is more
concentrated. Several such siltstones in a side-stream are
known collectively as the Deerhope Coral Bed. Good

exposures of the overlying Cock Rig Formation and the highly fossiliferous lower member of the Wether Law Linn Formation can be studied higher up this valley, but return to the North Esk to continue the succession.

9. River North Esk: Deerhope Formation—Upper

A large cutting in the river exposes a considerable thickness of siltstones near the top of the Cock Rig Formation, which forms beds 5–10 cm thick. These show tool marks indicating palaeocurrents from the east, and lineations on the bedding planes due to erosive current scour. Fossils are concentrated in lags at the bases of some of the siltstone layers. The fauna is dominated by bivalves, gastropods, corals, crinoids and chonetid brachiopods (Lamont, 1954).

10. River North Esk: Cock Rig Formation

The contact between the Deerhope and the overlying Cock Rig Formations is well exposed only in the Deerhope Burn. It can also be located in the North Esk section by a change in sediment type, where blue-grey mudstones and siltstones give way to yellow-brown medium grained sandstones and interbedded conglomeratic horizons. The Cock Rig Formation is well exposed on the east bank and also in the quarry on the west bank. The conglomerates contain clasts of granite, porphyry, sub-basic lava, quartzite, red and black chert, and fine-grained sediment in poorly graded cycles up to 25 cm thick. Cross-bedding, showing a variety of current directions is well preserved. Towards the top of the Formation is a largely transported benthic fauna made up of crinoid ossicles, the brachiopod *Isorthis mackenziei* and the bivalve *Leptodesma*.

11, 12 and 13. Wether Law Linn: Wether Law Linn Formation—Lower and Middle Members

The abrupt change from red sandstones to the green, highly bioturbated sandy mudstones marks the start of the Wether Law Linn Formation. Patchy hillside outcrops on the south side of Wether Law Linn allow the contact to be located. The lowest member of the formation, well-exposed on the south bank of the burn contains abundant brachiopods

Skenidiodes lewisii, *Cyrtia exporrecta*, *Dicoelosia verneuiliana* and subsidiary *Eoplectodonta penkillensis*, *Leptaena* aff. *purpurea* and the rugose coral (?) *Streptelasma* sp. Above a 20 cm white clay band representing the sudden deposition of volcanic ash, this fauna was replaced by a new and rich assemblage dominated by *Eoplectodonta penkillensis*. The brachiopods *Visbyella visbyensis* and *Leptaena* aff. *purpurea* together with the trilobites *Acernaspis sufferta* and *Encrinurus expansus* (other trilobites are less common) are numerous at the base of this assemblage but decrease in numbers up the succession. Correspondingly there is an increase in abundance of the gastropods *Gyronema* (?) *salteri* and *Liospira* (?) *simulans*, the bivalve *Synek* (?) sp., and the inarticulate brachiopods *Lingula* sp. and *Trimerella* cf. *visbyensis*. Gradually brachiopods similar to those of the topmost Cock Rig and lowermost Wether Law Linn Formations return at the top of the Lower Member. The fauna above the *Eoplectodonta* assemblage is best seen in a series of cuttings at (12) in the River North Esk.

The Middle Member of the Wether Law Linn Formation forms a large outcrop on the north bank of Wether Law Linn (13). These are yellow-brown laminated siltstones and fine sandstones, characterised by marked spheroidal weathering. The sparse fauna of cephalopod and graptolite remains is almost totally lacking in benthic elements.

14 and 15. Henshaw Burn: Wether Law Linn Formation—Upper Member

The Upper Member of the Wether Law Linn Formation is exposed (14) in a number of outcrops where the Henshaw Burn merges with the River North Esk. These are brownish well-laminated uniform siltstones and mudstones and contain a rather sparse restricted fauna dominated by varying elements through the succession. Up-section there are the nuculoid bivalve *Praearca kosoviensis*, the gastropod *Spirina antiquata*, the brachiopod *Pentlandella pentlandica* and ultimately the gastropod (?) *Liospira simulans*.

In a shallow trench (15) the contact between marine Wether Law Linn Formation and the overlying fluviatile-terrestrial Henshaw Formation is exposed. Pyrite-bearing fossiliferous silty mudstones grade into yellow, then red mudstones. Above these is a marked change to reddened grits of the Henshaw Formation. Strong evidence of contemporaneous leaching and precipitation is clear.

16. River North Esk: Henshaw Formation—Igneous Conglomerate

Conglomerates of the lower Henshaw Formation are well exposed on both sides of the River North Esk. This is the "Igneous Conglomerate" and contains clasts, up to cobble-size, of granite, porphyry, trachyte, sub-basic lava, siltstone and mudstone in bedded units of up to 1 m thick. Overlying these coarse conglomerates are reddened medium-grained sandstones showing occasional trough crossbeds.

17. Henshaw Burn: Henshaw Formation—Quartzite Conglomerate

An exposure of a 1·5 m thick bed of the "Quartzite Conglomerate" is exposed here which may be correlated with quartzite conglomerates found in the other Midland Valley Silurian Inliers. This conglomerate is markedly different from the Igneous Conglomerate containing approximately 70% quartzite clasts.

To return, follow the river bank to the reservoir. Alternatively join the Carlops-Balerno footpath which passes the cottage at the south-west corner of the reservoir.

Excursion B—Gutterford Burn

The object of this excursion is to study several famous localities in the Gutterford Burn within the Reservoir Formation. The starting point is also the cottage at the south-west end of the North Esk Reservoir.

18. Reservoir Formation—Lowest Beds

Good exposures of the Reservoir Formation, noted in Excursion A along the east bank (3) and north bank (4) of the North Esk Reservoir, continue up the Gutterford Burn which flows into the north-east corner of the reservoir. Purple and green finely laminated silty shales are inter-bedded with discrete beds 1 cm to 1 m thick, of siltstone and fine sandstone, sparsely fossiliferous. The stream runs roughly parallel to the strike allowing individual beds to be followed for long distances.

19. Reservoir Formation—Graptolite Beds

Purple and grey mudstones further upstream have yielded rare specimens of the smooth-shelled brachiopod *Lissatrypa atheroidea* and of several species of graptolites. The fauna is dominated by *Monoclimacis vomerinus* (s.l.) possible *M. crenulata* (sensu Elles & Wood) with occasional *Monograptus priodon* and *M. spiralis* and up to three species of dendroid graptolites. Precise identification is difficult but the fauna indicates a pre-Wenlock age for the Reservoir Formation.

20. Reservoir Formation—Gutterford Burn Limestone

Some siltstone to fine sandstone beds higher in the formation have thin basal lags of crinoid ossicles. One such bed which has a rich fossil content making it a highly calcareous siltstone, is known as the Gutterford Burn Limestone. Its outcrop can only be found with difficulty high on the eastern bank of the valley. It is a 25 cm thick lag deposit containing abundant broken corals and bryozoans, disarticulated brachiopods and bivalves, together with gastropods, trilobites, ostracods and crinoid ossicles draped over internal sedimentary structures.

21. Reservoir Formation—Eurypterid Bed

The next large outcrop upstream is the site of the Eurypterid Bed. These arthropod bearing laminated siltstones are dominated by stylonurids (Waterston, 1979) and contain one of the most extensive eurypterid faunas in the world. As a result of extensive excavations by Laurie (1892, 1899) the bed is now buried beneath a large pile of debris, but occasional fragments of the siltstones, along with abundant *Dictyocaris*, are to be found in the scree.

22. Fairliehope-Gutterford Intrusion

In the next large outcrop the sediments are cut by the Fairliehope-Gutterford Intrusion. It is necessary to examine the outcrop closely to differentiate igneous rock from baked siltstone. The intrusion is folded by tight F_1 folds producing three separate outcrops in the Gutterford Burn, formerly taken to be three separate intrusions. The intrusion is pre-Old Red Sandstone in age, since the body is affected by Silurian folding. From a position high on the north bank of the stream these tight F_1 folds can be seen to be themselves folded by younger more open F_2 kink folds of the kind exposed on the east bank of the reservoir (locality 3).

23 and 24. Reservoir Formation—Starfish Beds

Two starfish localities have been recorded high in the Gutterford Burn. The first (23) is on the north bank 100 m downstream from the wall across the burn and the second (24) on the south bank 50 m upstream from the wall, is the classic starfish bed of Peach and Horne (1899). The common starfish *Crepidosoma wenlocki* is found in fine micaceous silty shales with relatively rare brachiopods *Lissatrypa atheroidea*, *Clorinda*, hyolithids, cephalopods and the echinoid *Aptilechinus caledonensis*.

To return, it is easiest to follow the path high on the east bank of the burn back to the reservoir.

Excursion C—Lyne Water

The object of this excursion is to examine the Wether Law Linn Formation and to study the various alluvial facies in the terrestrial Henshaw Formation which are better developed than in the River North Esk. The starting point is the bridge at the north-east corner of the Baddinsgill Reservoir. The walking distance is approximately 4 km and should occupy at least 3 hours.

25. Baddinsgill Reservoir: Wether Law Formation— Upper Member

Strata of the Upper Member of the Wether Law Linn Formation crop out 150 m beyond the bridge, in the small side stream that flows into the reservoir. The yellow-brown muddy siltstones contain *Pentlandella pentlandica* and (?)*Liospira simulans*. On the south side of the stream a vertical fault throws the mudstones to the south, up against Lower Old Red Sandstone conglomerates. Contact with the Henshaw Formation near the bridge on the north bank of the reservoir is not here exposed.

26. Baddinsgill Reservoir: Henshaw Formation— Igneous Conglomerate

Along the north shore of the reservoir the Igneous Conglomerate is interbedded with thick beds of red medium-grained sandstones. The well-rounded hematite-stained pebbles of granite, porphyry, trachyte, sub-basic lava and fine-grained sediments form beds up to 50 cm thick. Moving along the shore of the reservoir the red sandstones become dominant. These contain isolated pebbles and thick pebble horizons, mainly composed of quartzite. Trough crossbedding is poorly developed.

27. Lyne Water: Henshaw Formation—Lyne Water Fish Bed

Above the red sandstones grey-green muddy siltstones are developed, displaying dessication cracks. On the east bank of the Lyne Water, 25 m north of the sheepfold, is the Lyne Water Fish Bed. These yellow-brown and grey laminated siltstones contain rare small broken fish fragments, mainly *Ateleaspis tessellata*, with some *Lasanius problematicus* and *Birkenia elegans*, as well as the crinoid *Pisocrinus campana* and worm tubes, probably representing a minor marine incursion.

Overlying the fish-beds are red medium-grained sandstones with well-developed trough crossbeds and quartzite pebbles, well-exposed since the Lyne Water runs along strike.

28. Lyne Water: Henshaw Formation, Unconformity

Red trough crossbedded medium-grained sandstones form the highest Silurian sediments exposed in the inlier. Gently northward dipping Lower Old Red Sandstone conglomerate is exposed above the Silurian-Old Red Sandstone unconformity.

29. Lynslie Burn: Henshaw Formation—Lyne Water Fish Bed

Retrace one's steps and proceed up the Lynslie Burn. Red sandstones give way to interbedded red siltstones and shales. Low amplitude ripples indicate some palaeocurrent directions. Near the junction with the Lynslie Burn there is a further outcrop of the Lyne Water Fish-Bed, formerly regarded as a separate higher fish bed, the Lynslie Burn Fish Bed (Mykura & Smith, 1962).

30. Lynslie Burn: Wether Law Linn Formation— Lower Member

Nearer the head of the Lynslie Burn on the north bank is a good fossil-collecting locality in the Lower Member of the Wether Law Linn Formation (locality 11). To return it is easiest to descend the valley back to the reservoir.

G. ROBERTSON

SOUTH QUEENSFERRY—CRAMOND

O.S. 1:50000 Sheet 65 Falkirk and West Lothian
B.G.S. 1:50000 Sheet 32W Livingston
Route: Maps 24 and 25

THE object of the excursion is to study the Dinantian oil-shale bearing sediments of West Lothian, as exposed along the coast from South Queensferry to Cramond, and to look at relics of the vast industry based on exploitation of the oil-shale. Also well displayed are teschenite sills of Namurian age and quartz-dolerite sills of Stephanian age, and their intrusive relationships to the sediments.

The area lies near the centre of the basin in which the oil-shale bearing beds were deposited. The basin was open to the north-east, from which direction sediment was derived, and cut off by Lower Palaeozoic rocks of the Southern Uplands to the south-east. In other directions it was enclosed by volcanic piles. In the cyclical sediments the lagoonal oil-shales are underlain by marine or freshwater limestones and mudstones and succeeded by thick mudstone-siltstone-sandstone sequences of fluvio-deltaic origin. Coals are rarely developed. The strata are divided into the Lower and the Upper Oil-Shale groups (Carruthers *et al.* 1927), the boundary being taken at the base of the freshwater Burdiehouse Limestone. The rocks belong to the Asbian and Brigantian Stages of the Viséan. The main marine marker band is the lowest widespread marine horizon in the local Carboniferous, the Pumpherston Shell Bed. It is found throughout West Lothian and is recognised in Midlothian and East Lothian as the Macgregor Marine Bands and Cove Marine Bands (Wilson 1974). Beds below and including the Pumpherston Shell Bed belong to the TC miospore zone, higher beds to the NM zone.

Four half-day excursions are listed, which can be combined to make one or two day excursions. Excursion A is the Paraffin Young Heritage Trail which starts at Grangemouth.

186

Leaflets describing the route should be obtained beforehand from the Forth Valley Tourist Board, County Buildings, Linlithgow, West Lothian, EH49 7EZ. The other excursions start either from South Queensferry where ample parking is available on the promenade west from Hawes Pier, or from Cramond where there is a large car park in the village. South Queensferry can be reached by Eastern Scottish service buses and Cramond is served by Lothian Region Transport buses. Travellers planning to use the Cramond Ferry should note the timetable (currently till 1900 in summer, 1600 in winter—not Fridays). Notice should also be taken of the landowner's requirement that no picnics be taken, or picnic haversacks carried between the Cramond Ferry and Long Craig Gate. While the sections are seen best when the tide is low, most exposures on the coastal excursions are near High Water Mark (HWM).

Excursion A—Paraffin Young Heritage Trail

The trail was established by Lothian Regional Council and BP Oil Grangemouth Refinery Ltd to depict the story of this remarkable man and the West Lothian shale oil industry. The trail starts at BP Oil Grangemouth and winds for 60 km along the side roads of West Lothian by seven information notice boards.

BP Oil Grangemouth (NS 941 814): Information Centre

Travel by the M9 Motorway to Grangemouth. Turn off at Junction 5 and follow the B9143 (Grangemouth Industry). Turn left at the first roundabout, right at the second roundabout, then after 50 m right into the BP car park. The Information Centre (open Monday to Friday, 0900 to 1700) houses an exhibition of the shale industry, a contemporary documentary film of mining in the 1920's and an exhibition of the modern oil industry.

1. Bathgate (966 673): An Industry is Born, the Secret Works

This house on the road south of Bathgate, once his secret laboratory, is all that remains of Young's original oil-works. It opened in 1851 using torbanite, and only later was attention turned to using oil-shale.

2. Five Sisters (NT 005 641): The Story of a Bing

The Westwood Bing, viewed from the B7015, is typical of the massive red spent shale spoil-heaps, produced from retorting the oil-shale. The substantial remains of the Westwood Works are still occupied by other enterprises. The five 'peaks' of the bing result from the method of tipping, green swards being from recent restoration.

3. Limefield House (034 643): Paraffin Young, his Life and Times

James Young lived in this pleasant mansion, now an old folks' home, just south of the A71 at Polbeth. The miniature Victoria Falls across the nearby stream commemorates his lifelong friendship with the missionary, David Livingstone.

4. Pumpherston (071 695): A Central Refinery

Pumpherston is a shale village built by the Pumpherston Oil Company. The company retorts and refinery, below the bings east of the village, are still the site of oil-related manufacture and the production of bricks from spent shale. In contrast along the banks of the River Almond nearby lies the beautiful wooded Almondell Country Park.

5. Middleton Hall (061 716): Scottish Oils Headquarters

Just south of the A89 in Uphall, the Hall stands surrounded by housing, originally built for oil company technical and managerial staff.

6. Broxburn (080 722): Shaleopolis

The story of how the shale industry transformed Broxburn from a small rural village to an industrial boom town with rows of brick-built houses is detailed on the trail noticeboard in the centre of the town on the A899.

7. Winchburgh (088 748): A Shale Company Village

The B8020 passes through one of the largest shale bings and by the road the final trail point describes this typical mining village with its high quality brick-built miners' rows.

5. Sill of white trap, altered basalt, intruding Upper Oil-Shale Group
sedimentary rocks, South Queensferry

Excursion B—South Queensferry Shore
(Route: Map 24)

The shore section exposes westerly dipping sediments of the Upper and Lower Oil-Shale groups, including oil-shales, limestones and marine and non-marine shell beds. Sills of white trap cut the sediments while further east are the Mons Hill teschenite sill and the Hound Point quartz-dolerite sill. The excursion starts at the Hawes Pier opposite the Hawes Inn (featured in R. L. Stevenson's *Kidnapped*).

1. Hawes Pier: Dunnet Sandstone

The pier and the south end of the Forth Railway Bridge (opened 1889) are built on the 90 m thick Dunnet Sandstone. Best seen just east of the bridge, the beds consist of pale brown and brown, fine to medium-grained, massive and cross-bedded deltaic sandstones. Layers in the sandstone contain ochreous plant stems and debris. U-shaped burrows near the top indicate local marine inundation. Sand-filled *Stigmaria*, hair-roots, sun-cracks and worm tracks show periodic exposure to air and establishment of forests. The steep dip of the basal sandstones is associated with faulting.

2. Port Neuk: Camps Shale, Burdiehouse Limestone

East of the sandstone outcrop poor exposures of the dark fissile Camps Shale and the hard grey Burdiehouse Limestone can be found among the shingle. The limestone has numerous ostracods, fish and plant fragments, and near LWM it has been bored by modern molluscs.

3. East of Port Neuk: Sill, White Trap, Algal Limestone

The foreshore on the east of the bay is formed of thick brown and white fine to medium-grained deltaic sandstones showing various bedding structures. Near the top a brown-weathered pale grey altered dolerite sill, 90 cm thick, can be distinguished from the sandstone by polygonal jointing. Sun-cracks are prominent in the underlying dark baked sandstone near the sea-wall. In the cliff 40 m further east is a striking outcrop of 'white trap', a sill of completely altered dolerite. The pale 60 cm thick sill, while generally concordant, also shows transgressive junctions with the dark hornfelsed

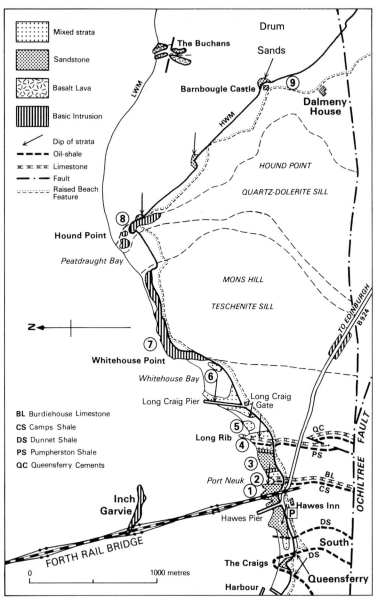

MAP 24. South Queensferry

sediments above and below. Thin dolerite sills intruded into carbonaceous mudstones, oil-shales or coals can become altered to white trap. The rock now consists mainly of carbonates of lime, magnesia and iron, kaolin and muscovite, but the original crystal structure of the dolerite can be seen in ordinary light under the microscope. Heat from the intrusion drove off from the carbonaceous beds by destructive distillation gases which altered the minerals in the dolerite.

A metre thick pale brown fine-grained ripple-bedded sandstone lies between the white trap and 1·1 m of thin finely laminated lagoonal cementstones which crop out round the point. Prominent algal patches near the top have rounded upper surfaces and flat bases. Lower down a thin desiccation breccia indicates drying out. Minor thrust faults at the point have caused fracturing with slickensides in sandstones and cementstones, but folding in the mudstones.

4. West of Long Rib: Mudstones, Pumpherston Shale

Underlying the cementstones are 25 m of dominantly argillaceous strata well-exposed in cliffs and foreshore. A marine mudstone 8 m from the top contains the bivalve *Naiadites obesus* and the branchiopod *Euestheria sp.* Near the base, just west of the small stream, the Pumpherston Shale, seams of economic oil-shale with thin ironstone ribs, forms three prominent reefs.

Oil-shales can be identified in the field by the following characteristics: a brown streak or brown colour when scratched instead of the grey of normal mudstones, a toughness and resistance to weathering, a leathery appearance, a wooden sound when hammered, and parings cut with a knife curl up and do not crumble. Oil-shales have been classed as plain, in which the bedding is regular, or curly, in which the bedding shows penecontemporaneous contortion.

5. Long Rib: Pumpherston Shell Bed, Queensferry Cements

East of the stream the Pumpherston Shell Bed occurs in strata locally with steep to vertical dips. The shell bed comprises a 50 cm soft dark mudstone with yellow sulphurous efflorescence on a 3 cm limestone, both parts of which can be traced towards LWM. The fauna, mostly pyritised in the mudstones, includes the bivalves *Aviculopecten*, *Pernopecten*, *Pteronites*, *Sanguinolites*, *Schizodus* and *Streblopteria*, small *Lingula*, the gastropod *Euphemites*, orthocone nautiloids and ostracods.

Below a further metre of dark mudstones, two cement-stones, the Queensferry Cements, form Long Rib, a conspicuous ridge running out to sea. The upper bed is a 35 cm yellow-weathering oolitic cementstone. The intervening grey mudstone is a metre thick. The lower cementstone is 1·2 m thick, is brown-grey but weathers yellow, and has cavities, some filled with bitumen.

Mudstones below the Queensferry Cements contain further cementstones and thin oil-shales. A 15 cm bedded cementstone forming an overhang in the cliff has mudstone flakes and brown coprolites containing fish fragments. Contorted mudstone just above this band could indicate a bedding-plane fault. The oil-shales include the Dalmahoy Shale, the lowest named oil-shale in the West Lothian shale field. The strata are mostly obscured by shingle towards Long Craig Pier, which is built on hard brown fine-grained sandstones dipping westwards at 25°.

6. Whitehouse Bay: Metamorphosed Sediments

Shingle obscures most of the sediments in the bay. Near HWM 300 m east of Long Craig Gate, and opposite the grey hut on the road, are outcrops of greenish and greyish indurated spotted mudstones. These gently dipping strata were baked by the underlying teschenite sill, but the contact is obscured.

7. Whitehouse Point: Mons Hill Teschenite Sill

Outcrops of a differentiated teschenite sill form a kilometre of rocky foreshore between Whitehouse Bay and Peatdraught Bay. Detailed petrographic descriptions of the sill are given by Flett (in Peach *et al*. 1910) and by Walker (1923), who recognised several zones or modifications in a sill over 100 m thick. Joints however indicate that the sill dips gently and undulates and suggest it is much thinner, so that some of the zones may be lateral equivalents. Seen in descending order the principal rock-types are:

DARK medium-grained theralite, small kersutite needles, undulating top surface, angular joints, black and pink segregation veins; fairly sharp unchilled junction.

COMPACT mottled sub-ophitic teschenite, angular joints; sharp basal contact at Whitehouse Point.

COARSE to very coarse-grained mottled augite-teschenite, purple ophitic titanaugite crystals up to 15 cm × 1 cm, analcimised plagioclase, chlorite, pink segregation veins and druses with zeolites, rounded joints; forms main bulk of sill between Whitehouse Point and the next point to the east.

DARK sub-ophitic augite-teschenite, angular joints: supposed to lie beneath the main part of sill, but may lie above it.

PALE medium-grained theralite, small kersutite needles.

COARSE-GRAINED hornblende-teschenite, nepheline absent; seen just east of small stack; sharp unchilled junction.

DARK medium-grained augite-teschenite, idiomorphic titanaugite crystals, angular joints; base obscured by sand.

8. Hound Point: Quartz-dolerite Sill

Sand in Peatdraught Bay covers sediments between the Monds Hill Sill and the Hound Point Sill. On the coast the westerly-dipping Hound Point quartz-dolerite sill is 20 to 30 m thick but thickens inland. Fine-grained blue-grey dolerite near the sill top is exposed in reefs near LWM. The bulk of the sill is dark medium-grained, columnar-jointed quartz-dolerite. East of Hound Point dark indurated mudstone with plant remains and fish scales is intercalated in the lower part of the sill. The base is transgressive and the underlying sandstone baked and tilted.

The excursion can be completed by returning along the inland track, or by continuing eastwards for Excursion C to Cramond.

Excursion C—Cramond Shore
(Route: Maps 24 and 25)

Along this stretch of coast the interest includes sedimentary sequences and structures, intrusions and their contacts, raised beaches and the buried channel of the River Almond. This excursion follows on from Excursion B, or can be reached by crossing the Cramond Ferry and taking the path to Snab Point, Barnbougle Castle or Hound Point.

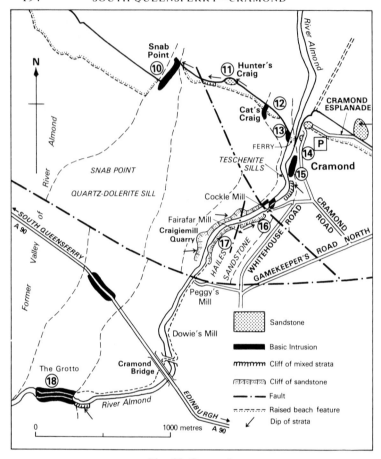

MAP 25. Cramond

9. Barnbougle Castle, Dalmeny House: Raised Beach, Buried Channel

Westward-dipping brown fine-grained sandstones crop out at HWM 800 m east of Hound Point and at Barnbougle Castle. The Buchans, reefs near LWM, are formed of green and purple amygdaloidal columnar basalt lava and red, brown and grey sandstone. The post-Glacial raised beach with its well-defined back-feature is narrow as far as

Barnbougle Castle and widens out in front of Dalmeny House. This magnificent Tudor-Gothic style house was built in 1815 by William Wilkins for the Earl of Roseberry. It contains the Roseberry and Mentmore collections and is open during afternoons in summer. The statue is the horse King Tom. Low ground south-east of the house lies along the pre-glacial channel of the River Almond blocked by glacial deposits.

10. Snab Point: Quartz-dolerite Sill, Sedimentary Sequence

Leaving the low raised beach, the path climbs sharply up the dip slope of the Snab Point quartz-dolerite sill. The top of the sill forms a dramatic slope of hard, black well-jointed dolerite dipping WNW at 25° into the sea. Just east of Snab Point the basal contact of the sill against baked mudstones is exposed at HWM.

Starting 200 m east of the sill is a cliff section of sedimentary rocks, dipping westwards at 15°. The highest 3 m comprises thin brown sandstones overlying grey mudstones and siltstones with plant fragments and irony ribs and nodules. Below these a 15 cm coal seam is underlain by 5 cm of grey seatclay. Most of the section is formed of a massive brown sandstone, 8·5 cm thick, showing large-scale cross-bedding. Loose blocks have fine rippled surfaces. The lowest 9 m of the section consists of grey siltstones with bands of pale brown sandstone.

11. Eagle Rock or Hunter's Craig: Sandstone

As well as the historical interest, for the defaced figure of an eagle carved on the rock is supposed to be of Roman origin, the stack demonstrates sedimentary structures of a fluvio-deltaic sandstone. The main face shows 3·6 m of laminar sandstone on 1·8 m of cross-bedded sandstone with an irregular 5 cm irony rib along the junction. On the seaward side are ancient ripples similar to modern ripples in the beach sand. Another rock further west shows 3 m of slumped contorted sandstone on 1·8 m of laminar and cross-bedded sandstone.

12. Cat's Craig: Teschenite Sill

Looking at first like an old stone wall the craig is the out-crop of the thin upper leaf of a teschenite sill. During post-Glacial raised beach times the craig formed an intertidal reef.

13. Coble Cottage: Teschenite Sill

The ferry house and jetty stand on a cliff formed by the lower leaf of the teschenite sill, the same rock-type that forms Cramond Island offshore. Coble Cottage sits on the middle of three raised beaches on the west side of the River Almond. Cross the river by the ferry and visit Cramond Heritage Trail Centre.

Excursion D—Almond Valley
(Route: Map 25)

This excursion follows along the pleasant riverside walks of the Cramond Heritage Trail. The geomorphology of the Almond valley can be studied as well as thick sandstones, complex sills and their contacts. The excursion starts at the Heritage Trail Centre, near the ferry landing point.

14. Cramond Heritage Trail Centre: Ravelston Sandstone, Raised Beaches

On the path outside the centre is a pale brown cross-bedded sandstone correlated with the Ravelston Sandstone. Two raised beaches east of the River Almond are evidence of higher sea-levels. The lower, post-Glacial, beach forms the terrace with a steep back slope on which the promenade stands. Material from the higher late-Glacial beach can be seen on the banks behind Cramond Boat Club, consisting of brown silty clay with pebbles, numerous oyster shells and a few *Pecten* and gastropod shells.

15. Quarries: Sill-sediment Relationships

Quarried cliffs above the path show two thin teschenite sills, the upper at least 3·5 m thick, the lower 1·8 m thick, dipping at 30° to north-west. The 60 cm mudstone between the sills has a pale grey hard baked ceramic look and has been welded on top of the lower sill. Below the teschenite is a white rusty-mottled fine-grained sandstone over 8 m thick, well exposed in a quarried face. Vertical drill holes at the north end are relics of the quarrying. At the weir the mill-lade has been cut into a further outcrop of teschenite.

16. Cockle Mill Weir: Hailes Sandstone, Faulting

Beyond the weir is a long 5 m high quarried face of sandstone dipping east. Note the change of dip from the previous outcrop, due to a fault just above the weir. The cliff of pale brown, part thinly bedded, part large-scale cross-bedded sandstone is broken up by two fault zones of disturbed rock. A prominent 30 cm dark purple band is hematite-stained sandstone.

17. Fairafar Iron Mill: Hailes Sandstone Gorge

At first sight looking as if built with red sandstone, this ruined mill was in fact built of a local pale brown sandstone. The red irony skin was formed during operation of the foundry, and stones on the weir are similarly affected. For the next 300 m the river flows through a gorge with steep sandstone walls 10 m high. The pale brown sandstone shows laminar and cross-bedding. It was exploited in Craigiemill Quarry across the river. Glacial till forms the tree-covered upper slopes of the valley. Exposures of the dark clay till, with pebbles such as sandstone, dolerite and vein quartz, can be seen at the top of the upstream steps. Beyond the gorge thicker glacial till forms gentler valley sides, upriver of Peggy's Mill.

18. Grotto Gorge: Mudstones, Quartz-dolerite Sill, Buried Channel

Cross to the north side of the river at Cramond Bridge and take the path to the left opposite Willowbank to rejoin the riverside walk. At the start of the rock gorge a cliff of bedded mudstones can be seen on the opposite bank dipping at 15° to the west under the Snab Point quartz-dolerite sill. A fine view from the bridge shows the gorge cut in jointed quartz-dolerite dipping west. The sill forms ridges north and south of the river. Upstream the open valley marks thick glacial deposits which blocked the former valley of the Almond and forced the river to cut the rock gorge. Return to the A90 at Cramond Bridge or all the way to Cramond.

A. D. McADAM

RIVER AVON

O.S. 1:50000 Sheet 65 Falkirk and West Lothian
B.G.S. 1:63360 Sheet 31 Airdrie
B.G.S. 1:10560 Sheets NS 97 NE and NS 98 SE
Route: Map 26

THIS excursion illustrates the pattern of sedimentation within the Passage Group (Namurian) on the margins of the Kincardine Basin, a major depositional centre of Carboniferous sediments. The localities are situated on the gently dipping, eastern limb of the Clackmannan Syncline, mainly in natural sections in the River Avon gorge between Grangemouth and Linlithgow. Bedrock is covered by thick deposits of Late-Devensian till, with mounds and eskers of glaciofluvial sand and gravel. Marine outwash deltas of clay, silt and sand and raised tidal flats of Late-Devensian and Flandrian age flank the Forth. The whole area has been affected by isostatic uplift resulting in cutting of the gorge of the River Avon since the end of the last glaciation. The excursion also gives insight into underground mining methods and the problems that ancient mine workings can create in an urban area.

Birkhill Mine may be reached from Linlithgow via the A706 and from Bo'ness and Grangemouth via the A904. Leave the public roads at Upper Kinneil Farm (NS 974 793) and travel WSW down the metalled single track road. Continue SSE on to the unmetalled road into the former mine and park beyond the cottages at the mine buildings. Coaches can follow this route but the roads are narrow with few passing places. For access to the former mine, contact the custodian, preferably in advance, who will unlock the safety doors and escort visitors around. Hard hats, powerful torches and wellington boots are required. The main part of the excursion is compact and it is easy to walk to the localities from the mine buildings (Map 26). Locality 9, 1·5 km away, and locality 10 at Bo'ness, about 6 km away, are optional but of

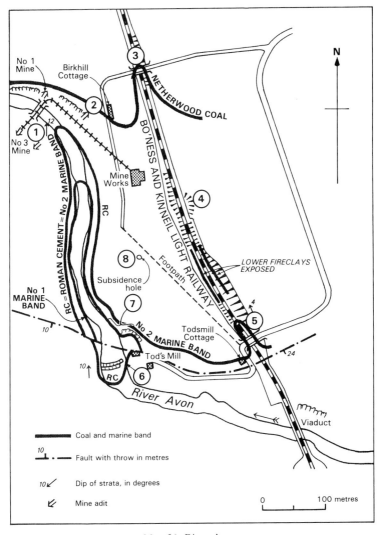

N

No 1 Mine

Birkhill Cottage

No 3 Mine

③

②

①

12

NETHERWOOD COAL

BO'NESS AND KINNEIL LIGHT RAILWAY

RC = ROMAN CEMENT = No 2 MARINE BAND

No 2 MARINE BAND

RC

Mine Works

④

LOWER FIRECLAYS EXPOSED

Footpath

No 1 MARINE BAND

10

⑧

Subsidence hole

⑦

4

⑤

Todsmill Cottage

24

Tod's Mill

10

RC

⑥

River Avon

Viaduct

Coal and marine band

10 ⊢⋅— Fault with throw in metres

10 ↙ Dip of strata, in degrees

↙ Mine adit

0   100 metres

MAP 26. River Avon

historical interest. There are plans by the Bo'ness Heritage
Trust to preserve the Birkhill Mine as a mining visitor centre
linked to Bo'ness by the Bo'ness and Kinneil Light Railway
(Scottish Railway Preservation Society). The woodlands
along the banks of the Avon are a botanical SSSI.

The sediments exposed in the gorge of the River Avon
consist of a series of upward-fining cycles, between 1·5 m and
12 m thick (Figure 20), thought to have been formed by the
migration of meandering rivers. Each cycle starts with a
disconformity formed by an erosive river channel. The
succeeding channel-fill sandstone becomes progressively
finer-grained as it is traced upwards and grades into silty or
clayey overbank, floodplain deposits. These muddy beds
range in colour from black, through dark grey and pale grey
to variegated lilac, dull red and ochreous yellow, the brighter
colours reflecting partial oxidation during periods of lowered
water table. The siltstones and mudstones are characteristi-
cally unstratified and contain stigmarian rootlets. The
mudstones are commonly refractory fireclay, some containing more than 40% of alumina as kaolinite, after ignition.
Read (1969) thought that the clay fraction may have been
derived from an area of bauxitic weathering. The marine
bands in the succession reflect widespread marine incursions
into the dominantly fluvial environment.

1. Birkhill No. 3 Mine

From the old works, descend by the footpath opposite the
former manager's cottage until it joins the old cable tramway
and then cross the bridge over the river, built wide enough to
allow foxhunts across. The mine adit is driven into the south
side of the Avon valley at the outcrop of the Lower Fireclays.
On entering the mine, in operation from 1932 to 1981, note
the height of the roadway and galleries of four to five metres.
Here the roof of the mine is formed by a very siliceous,
medium to coarse-grained, white sandstone, over 6 m thick,
a lithology which typifies the Passage Group. Powerful lamps
reveal in the sandstone roof many fossilised tree trunks
which collected together as log jams in the Namurian rivers.
Stumps of large trees can be seen rooted in the fireclay and
protruding upwards into the sandstone. About 125 m into the
mine the roof of the roadway rises abruptly to about 8 m and

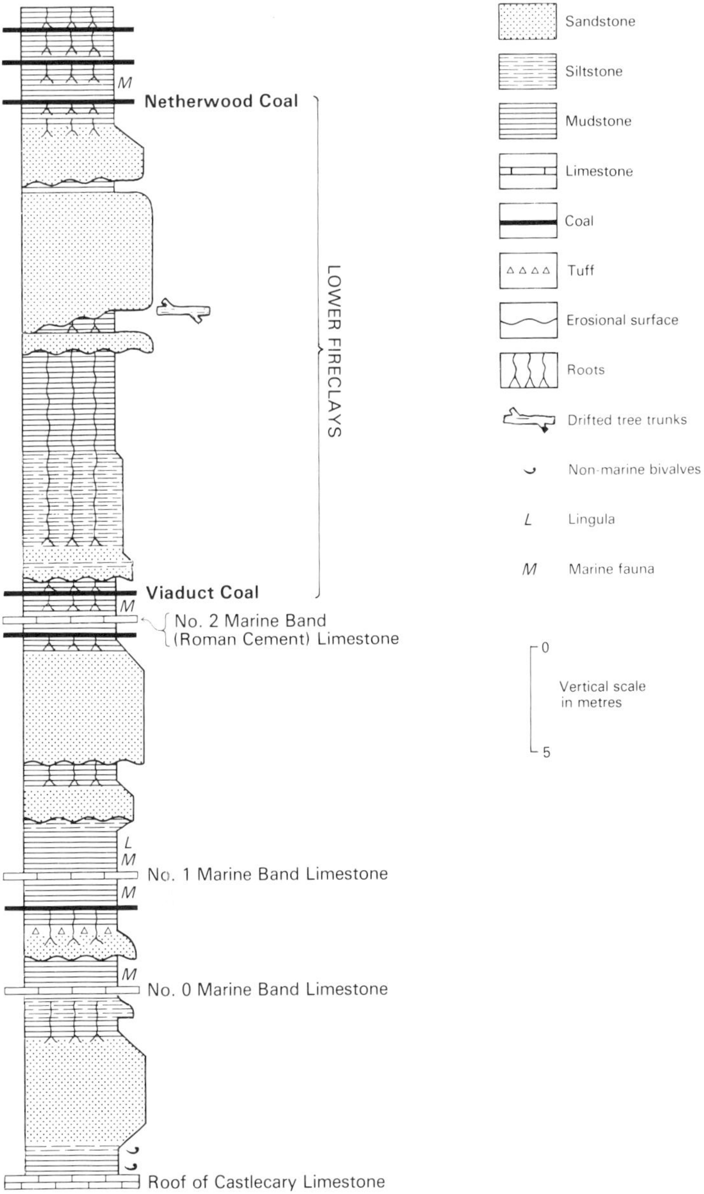

Netherwood Coal
LOWER FIRECLAYS
Viaduct Coal
No. 2 Marine Band
(Roman Cement) Limestone
No. 1 Marine Band Limestone
No. 0 Marine Band Limestone
Roof of Castlecary Limestone
M
L
Sandstone
Siltstone
Mudstone
Limestone
Coal
Tuff
Erosional surface
Roots
Drifted tree trunks
Non-marine bivalves
Lingula
Marine fauna
0
Vertical scale
in metres
5

FIG 20. Section in Passage Group

a fault, trending westwards with a downthrow to the north of 3 m, may be seen. A little farther on, just before the water-logged area of the mine, enter the side galleries to study the size of the rooms and the clay pillars left in to support the roof. This style of extraction is called stoop and room, or pillar and stall, working and about 40% of the seam is normally removed. The roof and floor of the mine are in good condition, the only noticeable erosion being where some blocks of clay have fallen from the walls.

2. Birkhill No. 1 Mine

Re-cross the River Avon, noting the sealed main entrance to No. 1 Mine on the north bank and walk up the tramway to the second entrance. *On no account venture far into this adit for the walls are in poor condition* and the sandstone roof is fissured and some falls have taken place. The mine was worked between 1916 and 1928. The section at the entrance to the mine is:

	metres
Sandstone, medium to very coarse-grained, with quartz pebbles, cross-stratified	7·0
Seatclay, grey, traces of stratification, dark carbonaceous root traces, many polished surfaces, ironstone nodules in top 60 cm	2·4
Clayrock, pale grey, root traces, many polished surfaces, some ironstone nodules at base	2·4

3. Birkhill Railway Cutting: Netherwood Coal

Ascend to the cottage, take the road out of the mine as far as the railway bridge and descend to the former track bed on the north-west side. At this bridge a section can be cleaned up to reveal:

	metres
Mudstone, soft, weathered, with productid brachiopods	0·45
NETHERWOOD COAL, dull	0·15
Seatrock, sand and silt grade, pale grey	
Sandstone, fine-grained, white, traces of cross-bedding	

4. Sandstone Quarry

In an old quarry 200 m to the south-east, and 20 m east of the cutting, is a section:

	metres
Sandstone, fine and medium-grained, cross-stratified; erosive base	1·65
Sandstone, fine-grained, planar and cross-stratified	0·22
Siltstone, micaceous, sandy layers, plant debris	0·05
Sandstone, fine-grained, planar and cross-stratified	0·86
Sandstone, fine and very fine-grained, ripples	0·25
Sandstone, medium-grained, cross-stratified	0·48

The Lower Fireclays below the sandstone are exposed in the cutting walls for almost one hundred metres from the south end of the quarry.

5. Todsmill Cottage: No. 2 Marine Band Limestone

At the southern end of the cutting, just before the bridge, a section in the north face can be cleaned up to expose:

	metres
Sandstone, medium-grained, rooty, trough cross-stratified with sharp rolling erosive base	1·00
Mudstone, grey, roots, traces of bedding	0·30
VIADUCT COAL, mainly dull banded, sand-filled casts of horizontal tree trunks at top	0·18
Seatclay, dark and pale grey, some irony nodules, many polished surfaces, dark roots	0·75
Mudstone, dark grey, fissile, packed with ironstone nodules	0·28
ROMAN CEMENT LIMESTONE (No. 2 Marine Band Limestone), dark grey, very muddy, many marine shells, mainly articulate brachiopods (exposed by trenching at trackbed level)	0·30
Mudstone, dark grey, bedded, irony nodules, some brachiopods	0·25

On a fine day, walk on to the Avon Viaduct for a view of the gorge eastwards to Linlithgow Palace. Before leaving the railway at Todsmill Cottage, pause to reflect that in 1916 the famous field surveyor, C. T. Clough of the Scottish Geological Survey, was run down and fatally injured by a goods train in this cutting. He died three days later but not before exonerating the driver from any blame. In view of the good visibility hereabouts, it seems likely that Clough's hearing impediment led to the tragedy.

6. Tod's Mill Weir

Walk westwards from Todsmill Cottage to Tod's Mill, descend to the river bed on the north side of the ruins of the mill and pass through the remains of the waterwheel. Just upstream of the mill and on the east bank near the weir is the section:

	metres
Seatclay, dark grey, dark roots, many clayband ironstone nodules (known as the Curdly Ironstone)	0·45
Nodular ironstone and limestone, pale grey, brown weathered, large marine shells	0·12
ROMAN CEMENT LIMESTONE, dark grey, muddy, lenticular, packed with crushed marine shells, mainly articulate brachiopods	0·18
Mudstone, dark grey, bedded, marine shells increase in frequency upwards, some irony nodules	0·40
COAL, dull banded, inferior	0·08
Seatrock, silt and sand grade, fining upwards, pale grey, dark roots	0·70
Sandstone, fine-grained, roots at top, cross-stratified; forms the weir across the river	2·40

7. Tod's Mill: River Cliff

Walk 30 m downstream of Todsmill to where the cliff reaches the river. At the waterwheel is the Tod's Mill Fault which throws 10 m down to the south. The section exposed north of the fault is:

	metres
Sandstone, fine and medium-grained, white, sharp base	3·00
Mudstone, dark grey, carbonaceous, coal laminae	0·15
Seatrock, pale grey, clay grade	0·33
Sandstone, fine and medium-grained, roots at top, flat bedded and planar cross-bedded	3·00
Mudstone, bedded, dark grey, weathered, abundant *Lingula*, many marine shells in lower part	1·40
NO. 1 MARINE BAND LIMESTONE, mainly dark grey, muddy, nodular in part, marine shells	0·48
Mudstone, dark grey, marine shells, sulphurous yellow weathered	0·96
COAL, dull, inferior	0·01
Seatrock, clay and silt grade, dark roots, hard irony top, large ironstone nodules, tuffaceous aspect with pale grey, angular tuff fragments	0·91
Ironstone, greenish grey, tuffaceous, pale greenish grey angular tuff fragments, sphaerosideritic	0·45
Seatrock, silt and clay grade, pale grey	0·45

8. Subsidence Hole

Retrace the way to Todsmill Cottage and follow the foot-path north-west from the railway bridge towards Birkhill Mine for 200 m. The ground has collapsed 20 m west of the path to form a sit or crown hole where the sandstone roof of

19th century fireclay workings has failed. The cone of depression is 9 m deep and 4 m wide with the fireclay visible in the wall at the bottom. It is not advised to try to enter the old workings through the hole at the bottom. Clearly if such a collapse occurred in a built-up area the damage to property might be severe (locality 10).

9. Craigenbuck Mine (NS 959 700)

This locality is adjacent to the A904 Bo'ness to Grangemouth road at the west end of the wood at Water Inns. The section is:

	metres
Sandstone, fine-grained, off-white cross-stratified	1·5
Mudstone, dark grey, bedded, hard irony bands, carbonaceous, fish remains, coprolites, *Curvirimula*	0·9
CASTLECARY LIMESTONE, not seen, could be excavated, loose blocks are of pale grey dolomitic limestone with rare algal nodules	2·1

The bituminous mudstone roof of the limestone is interesting because it contains only non-marine fossils, a feature typical of the Castlecary Limestone in central and eastern Scotland. Most marine limestones in the Upper Carboniferous sequence are overlain by mudstones with marine faunas. The limestone was used for mortar and flux at the former Kinneil Ironworks.

Following the southern field boundary westwards for about 200 m from the mine entrance, the ploughed soil indicates the existence of several Kitchen Midden sites at least three of which have been partially excavated. The middens locally are up to three metres deep and consist almost entirely of oysters, and a few mussels and periwinkles. The middens are probably about 6000 years old and date from the time when the Flandrian sea washed the foot of the marked bluff in this field. This conspicuous cliff line forms the Flandrian 'Main Postglacial Shoreline', a raised beach which has been recognised extensively throughout the Forth area and is associated with the estuarine deposits of the Carse Clay.

10. Bo'ness Bus Station (NS 998 817): Subsidence

A sit formed in Bo'ness one Sunday in 1885 when the Town Hall subsided into old stoop and room workings in the

FIG 21. The Old Town Hall, Bo'ness, and stoop and room workings in the
Wester Main Coal 15 m below the Old Town Hall

Wester Main Coal (Limestone Coal Group) about 15 m below ground level (Figure 21). The site of the hall is now a landscaped area to the south of the Bus Station. No visit is complete without reading Cadell's account of the disaster (1925) and the text of the relevant biblical dissertation which was being delivered at the time (Luke, Ch. 13, v. 4) concerning the fall of the Tower of Siloam.

Acknowledgements

Without the unpublished, detailed field surveying of W. A. Read and J. M. Dean (BGS) prior to 1967, this account would not have been possible. The sections included herein are transcribed verbatim from their notebooks.

M. A. E. BROWNE

BATHGATE HILLS

O.S. 1:50000 Sheet 65 Falkirk and West Lothian
B.G.S. 1:63360 Sheet 31 Airdrie
B.G.S. 1:50000 Sheet 32W Livingston
Route: Map 27

THE Bathgate Hills owe their general elevation to the presence of a considerable thickness (up to 500 m) of hard, resistant volcanic rocks of basaltic composition. These replace much of the normal sequence of softer, less resistant, sedimentary rocks between the top of the Upper Oil-Shale Group and the middle of the Upper Limestone Group. Individual hills, often craggy, are formed by east-west trending dykes and inclined sills of the late-Carboniferous quartz-dolerite suite. Intercalated sediments within the volcanic pile include several limestones of both freshwater and marine origin. It is difficult to correlate these limestones with the established successions in sedimentary basins outside the Bathgate Hills. The thickest and most persistent limestone-bearing strata, the Petershill Formation, formed around an elevated volcanic land area lying to the north of Bathgate (Jameson 1980). Lateral changes in the lithology and fauna of these strata can be traced from the seaward side northwards towards the inferred land area.

The East Kirkton Limestone, in contrast to the Petershill Limestone, is of freshwater origin but demonstrates an unusual lithology which is thought to be associated with hot springs. These beds have yielded an important and distinctive flora and fauna. The limestones of the Bathgate Hills have been extensively worked in the past for agricultural use both by quarrying and mining. An example of the latter will be seen at Hillhouse.

The aims of the excursion are: (i) to contrast the sedimentology and palaeontology of the freshwater East Kirkton Limestone with those of the marine Petershill and Hillhouse limestones; (ii) to examine the intercalated basaltic tuffs and lava flows; (iii) to examine the late-Carboniferous quartz-dolerite intrusions; and (iv) to see the remains of 17th, 18th and 19th century silver-nickel-lead workings at Hilderston Mine. In Map 27 showing the route the geology is based upon recent mapping, boreholes and air-photo interpretation. The outcrops are all easily accessible from public roads, making visits by vehicle convenient, but they may be traversed on foot, in the order described, involving a 9 km walk from the first to last outcrop or 12 km between public transport centres in Bathgate and Linlithgow, both of which are on Eastern Scottish service bus routes.

1. East Kirkton Quarry: East Kirkton Limestone

Park at the gate to the quarry (NS 990 689). East Kirkton Quarry is presently the site of intensive scientific investigation and permission to visit must be obtained beforehand from Mr S. Wood, Mr Wood's Fossils, Unit 8, Abbotsford Rise, Livingston.

The East Kirkton Limestone is a laterally impersistent sedimentary sequence within a thick succession of basaltic lavas and tuffs. The lithological succession consists of limestone overlain by black mudstones (Muir and Walton 1957) but is laterally variable in detail. Within the limestone occur bands with contorted laminae, tuff horizons where spherulitic structures are common, and beds of impure limestone with chert nodules. These lithologies have been interpreted as having been laid down in shallow pools associated with hot springs.

The limestones have recently yielded an unusual flora and fauna including amphibians, millipedes, eurypterids, scorpions, the earliest known harvestman (opilionid) and much plant material (Milner 1985; Wood et al. 1985). The presence of these forms, together with a striking absence of fishes, suggests a palaeoecology where amphibians were an integral part of the terrestrial fauna. The black mudstones, lying stratigraphically above the limestone, are also associated with laterally impersistent bands of tuff and have yielded a fauna containing both ostracods and fish remains.

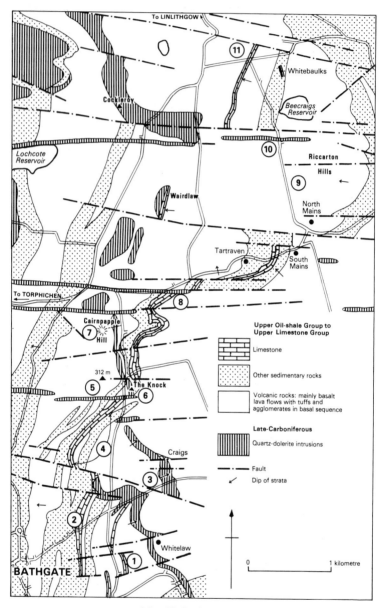

Upper Oil-shale Group to Upper Limestone Group

Limestone

Other sedimentary rocks

Volcanic rocks: mainly basalt lava flows with tuffs and agglomerates in basal sequence

Late-Carboniferous

Quartz-dolerite intrusions

--- Fault

↙ Dip of strata

0 1 kilometre

MAP 27. Bathgate Hills

2. Petershill Reservoir: Seaward Development of the Petershill Limestone

Park in rough lay-by at the bend in the road (985 694). On the east bank of the reservoir, the Petershill Limestone has a high carbonate content and is only slightly argillaceous. It was originally horizontally-bedded and contains an abundant fauna of solitary corals and low mounds of *Lithostrotion junceum* (a colonial coral giving rise to the popular name 'spaghetti rock'). The fauna also has delicate elements, epifaunal spinose productids and echinoids, which are well preserved with little disturbance, indicating quiet sedimentation. The trace fossil *Thalassinoides* is characteristic of this facies.

The southern wall of the reservoir is the central portion of a bioherm, built-up of successive beds composed mostly of skeletal remains. A three-part ecological succession shows a basal, small productid-fenestellid association with few species (low-diversity), passing up into a high-diversity productid-sponge-rostroconch association, replaced towards the top by an echinoderm-dominated association. The succession can be interpreted in terms of regional shallowing with regression and eventual exposure. About midway up the southern wall of the reservoir a thin (1–2 cm) impersistent band of clay can be seen. This is a bentonite horizon, consisting largely of montmorillonite formed from a weathered local ash fall.

3. Craigs: Quartz-dolerite Sill

Park 500 m west of Wester Drumcross (995 700); roadside parking may be difficult. A quartz-dolerite sill of the late-Carboniferous suite trends NNW-SSE across the hills. Here it dips moderately steeply ENE, contrary to the regional dip of the sediments and lavas, and forms a prominent west-facing scarp with brown, spheroidal-weathering outcrops. From the north of the road the scarp can be seen trending north-west towards Raven Craig. It is cut, and in some places displaced, by E-W trending valleys, interpreted as fault-lines scoured out by glacial action. A track follows the foot of the scarp northwards and eastwards for 300 m to the ruins of Craigs and a small quarry. Here, above the sill, 4 m of ill-sorted tuffs rest on 3·5 m of pale grey, well-bedded limestone

with shale partings and some tuffaceous bands. The rocks
show signs of baking and disturbance by the sill, the top contact of which may be traced in outcrops NNW of the ruins.
These are some of the few natural outcrops of the tuffs near
the base of the Bathgate Hills volcanic sequence, which are
known from boreholes to reach considerable thicknesses.
Other outcrops occur at Whitelaw (994 692), in a stream
(998 695) and in a roadside quarry (996 700). All are close to
the top of the sill and probably crop out owing to an increased resistance to erosion produced by contact meta-
morphism. Dips, where seen, tend to conform to the top of
the sill, rather than to the regional dip.

4. The Rifle Range Quarries: Landward Development of the Petershill Limestone

Park in the roadside quarry at The Knock (991 711). In the
Rifle Range Quarries, which extend south-west for a kilometre,
the Petershill Limestone consists of heterogeneous packstones,
medium-grained bioclastic limestones, located north and
palaeogeographically shoreward of the laterally equivalent
limestones exposed at the Petershill Reservoir (locality 2). In
the lower 3–4 m of the quarry-face, cross-stratified crinoidal
packstones, large cerioid coral colonies, bands of *Gigantoproductus* and large *Chaetetes* colonies can be seen. Although
most of the fauna is *in situ*, signs of extensive hydrodynamic influence on the original life-surfaces are present throughout the
sequence. Overturned corals with the open ends (calices) of the
corallites downwards and coral debris, as well as separated and
stacked brachiopod shells all suggest that currents were at times
a major destructive force. The heterogeneous packstone facies
is interpreted as having accumulated in a relatively turbulent,
nearshore zone.

At the northern end of the quarries, a blue-grey basalt lava
flow rests directly upon the limestone. The quarries termi-
nate at a vertical E-W dyke of quartz-dolerite which exhibits
good columnar jointing perpendicular to its margins.

5. Triangulation Station (987 712): Basaltic Lavas of Dalmeny Type

To the north-west of the north end of the limestone
quarries (locality 4), several low scarp features trend NNE

across the hillside as far as the triangulation point. Outcrops on these features are of a fresh, fine-grained, blue-grey basalt—the hard, central parts of lava flows. The basalts appear non-porphyritic, but in thin-section abundant 1 mm microphenocrysts of fresh olivine show them to be of Dalmeny type (MacGregor 1928). The presence of abundant interstitial analcime suggests gradation from olivine-basalt to basanite. Between the scarp features, topographic hollows with no exposure are due mainly to rubbly, altered flow tops or may in some cases indicate thin intercalations of sediment or pyroclastic horizons.

6. The Knock: Quartz-dolerite Sill, Viewpoint

Cross the road to The Knock, where the quartz-dolerite sill seen at locality 3, trends NNW and dips steeply ENE at 60°, probably marking a step-like transgression between stratigraphic levels. The sill forms the rocky knoll of The Knock and its top surface forms the steep slab on the east side. In the back wall of the quarry on the south-west side, the lower chilled contact is well exposed where it cuts blue-grey basalt lava dipping north-west at about 20°.

From the top of The Knock the regional geology of the Bathgate Hills and that of the Midland Valley as a whole may be appreciated. The underlying bedrock of the Midland Valley shows itself in the landforms, with the harder igneous rocks forming the hills and the softer sediments the lowland. Far to the north are the metamorphic rocks of the Grampian Highlands, with the andesitic lavas of the Ochil Hills in the middle distance. To the south-east, the Old Red Sandstone sediments and lavas of the Pentland Hills can be seen with the Lower Palaeozoic rocks of the Southern Uplands due south. Eastwards most of the prominent topographic features such as Arthur's Seat, the Bass Rock and North Berwick Law, all correspond to areas of igneous rock. Also to be seen are the flat-topped, red bings which are the remains of West Lothian's oil-shale industry and which pick out the outcrop of the Oil-Shale Groups. The oil-shale was mined and burned in large retorts to extract the hydrocarbons; the red bings are made up of the burnt oil-shale. Looking to the west, black conical bings can be seen. These are the spoil from coal mining and their distribution picks out the outcrop of the Coal Measures. Note the marked east-west valleys due to glacial scouring along fault-lines, and crag-and-tail features such as The Knock itself, which indicate west to east ice movement.

7. Hilderston Mine: Silver–Lead–Zinc Mineralisation

Park in the lay-by for Cairnpapple at the top of the hill (989 718). Immediately west of the road, the quartz-dolerite sill of localities 3 and 6 crops out forming a good N-S feature some 40 m wide. The sill dips steeply to the east as at The Knock, and is really a dyke-like step between levels of sill. A diversion may be made at this point to the bronze-age burial mound of Cairnpapple Hill, 250 m to the south-west, which is also a good viewpoint.

Follow the sill/dyke southwards into the valley to the ruins of Windywa's which are on the site of the original 17th century Hilderston silver mine (Cadell 1925, 359–378; Stephenson 1983). The mine was in operation initially from 1606 to 1614 but made little or no profit after the first two years (i.e. after it had been 'nationalised' by King James VI). The silver occurred in a vein as filaments of native silver in a gangue of baryte and niccolite. This vein was located on the margin of a thin E-W dolerite dyke which cut sandstones and siltstones above the Petershill Limestone. The economic vein extended for only 80 m to the east of the N-S dyke/sill and for 18 m below the surface. In the 18th century the mine was reopened and worked for lead and zinc which occurred within a baryte and calcite gangue at deeper levels, where the vein cut the Petershill Limestone. A second, much longer vein, some 60 m to the north, was also worked at this time, but this phase of working ceased in 1772. The original workings were re-excavated during the period 1865 to 1873 using money from the sale of the niccolite and again from 1896 to 1898. However, no further economic deposits of silver or lead were discovered.

The full list of known minerals from the mine is: baryte, calcite, dolomite, quartz, galena, sphalerite, niccolite, erythrite (nickel bloom), annabergite (cobalt bloom), bravoite, pyrite, chalcopyrite, albertite (solid hydrocarbon) and native silver. Most of these, with the exception of the nickel, cobalt and silver minerals, have been obtained recently from the waste heaps.

Three depressions close to the road at Windywa's mark the site of the main group of 17th century shafts. A large mound in the field east of the road marks the main 18th century shaft on the northern lead vein. The 1873 shaft is probably marked by a pile of debris, crescentic in plan, south of the burn and 35 m east of the road. Two adits in the west wall of the flooded Silvermines quarry mark two branches of the northern lead vein, probably excavated in the 19th century. If the water level is low, these adits can be examined. *Do not attempt to enter them.* Thin calcite veins with galena can be seen cutting the sandstone roof of the northernmost one.

The Petershill Limestone is no longer visible in the quarries, but the overlying clastic sediments can be examined in the cut to the south. Here an upward-coarsening sequence of clastic sediments can be seen with mudstone at the base of the quarry, gradually passing upwards to sandstone at the top. Fallen sandstone blocks at the foot of the quarry show good examples of trace fossils, both burrows and feeding trails. This type of upward-coarsening succession is typical of that associated with deltaic sedimentation. A thin N-S tholeiite dyke in the west wall of the southern quarry is altered to 'white trap' at its northern end.

8. North Mine Quarry: Petershill Limestone, Dyke

Park by the roadside (995 722). In the quarry, only massive sandstone is now seen, with a capping of basalt lava forming knolls in the plantation above the north face. An E-W dyke of quartz-dolerite, 30 m wide, forms a feature which is followed by the road. Just over the fence on the south side of the road, immediately east of the plantation, the southern contact of the dyke with the Petershill Limestone is exposed. The limestone contains colonies of *Lithostrotion* and is intensely baked. Both limestone and dolerite are impregnated with pink baryte. 'Copper ore' has also been recorded from this locality.

9. Riccarton Hills: Basalt Lavas

From North Mine drive east, past Tartraven (small, over-grown limestone quarries). At South Mains, take the road left (north) towards Beecraigs. From this road views are seen of good trap features in basalt lavas of the Riccarton Hills to the east.

10. Beecraigs Wood: Quartz-dolerite Dyke

Park at Beecraigs Country Park (NT 007 743) and walk south to the quarry on the west side of the road, cleared as a climbing wall. The face shows a section across an E-W quartz-dolerite dyke. The dolerite is very fresh and exhibits horizontal columnar jointing. The fine-grained edge of the dyke can be seen beside the ladder.

11. Hillhouse Quarry and Mine: Hillhouse Limestone

Park at Beecraigs Visitors' Centre (006 746), walk northwards and turn left at the T-junction. Quarries trend N-S on both sides of the road where the Hillhouse Limestone (possibly a lateral equivalent of the Petershill Limestone) has been worked by both surface and underground methods. The strata dip west at 30–40° and consequently the stoop and room workings north of the road, which are still open, slope very steeply undergound. *Do not enter these workings.* There have been roof collapses in recent years, some of which have caused subsidence in the overlying road.

The limestone is 9 to 12 m thick, the most complete section being exposed north of the road. Here the limestone is mostly massive with fossiliferous bands rich in crinoids, solitary and colonial corals and productid brachiopods. South of the road only 2 m of limestone is seen, overlain by over 2·5 m of cross-bedded sandstones and siltstones. The upper part of the section consists of a sill of very fresh basalt having well-developed, sub-vertical columnar joints. This sill is the type locality for the Hillhouse type of olivine-basalt (MacGregor 1928). The characteristic abundant microphenocrysts of olivine and augite are clearly visible on the weathered surfaces of the basalt.

D. STEPHENSON and S. K. MONRO

REFERENCES

General Geology

Principles of Physical Geology (third edition revised by Doris L. Holmes).
A. HOLMES. 1978. 730 pp. Van Nostrand Reinhold (UK).
The Cambridge Encyclopaedia of Earth Sciences. D. G. SMITH (Editor).
1981. 496 pp. Cambridge University Press.
A Dynamic Stratigraphy of the British Isles. R. ANDERTON, P. H. BRIDGES,
M. R. LEEDER and B. W. SELLWOOD. 1979. 301 pp. George Allen &
Unwin.
Sedimentology: Process and Product. M. R. LEEDER. 1982. 344 pp. George
Allen & Unwin.
Sedimentary Environments and Facies. H. G. READING (Editor). 1978. 569
pp. Blackwell.
Ancient Sedimentary Environments. R. C. SELLEY. 1970. 237 pp. Chapman
and Hall.
Volcanoes. P. FRANCIS. 1976. 368 pp. Penguin.
Guide to the practical study of crystals, minerals and rocks (revised first
edition). K. G. COX, N. B. PRICE and B. HARTE. 1972. 245 pp.
McGraw Hill.
The Country Life Guide to Minerals, Rocks and Fossils. W. R. HAMILTON,
A. R. WOOLLEY and A. C. BISHOP. 1974. 280 pp. Country Life.
Invertebrate palaeontology and evolution (second edition). E. N. K.
CLARKSON. 1986. 382 pp. George Allen and Unwin.
Atlas of Invertebrate Macrofossils. J. W. MURRAY (Editor). 1985. 241 pp.
Longman/The Palaeontological Association.
British Museum Handbooks. British Museum (Natural History). H.M.S.O.
  British Caenozoic Fossils
  British Mesozoic Fossils
  British Palaeozoic Fossils
Geological Museum Booklets. British Geological Survey. H.M.S.O.
  Britain before Man. F. W. DUNNING *et al.* 1978. 36 pp.
  British Fossils. J. THACKRAY. 1984. 36 pp.
  Earthquakes. S. VAN ROSE. 1983. 36 pp.
  The Age of the Earth. J. THACKRAY. 1980. 36 pp.
  The Geological Map. An anatomy of a Landscape. E. EDMONDS. 1984. 36 pp.
  The Origin and Evolution of Coal. P. J. ADAMS. 1983. 16 pp.
  The Story of the Earth. Anon. 1972. 36 pp.
  Volcanoes. S. VAN ROSE and I. MERCER. 1974. 36 pp.

Scottish Geology

The Geology of Scotland (second edition). G. Y. CRAIG (Editor). 1983.
472 pp. Scottish Academic Press.

217

Geology and Scenery in Scotland. J. B. WHITTOW. 1977. 362 pp. Penguin.

BRITISH REGIONAL GEOLOGY. British Geological Survey. H.M.S.O.

> *The Midland Valley of Scotland* (third edition). I. B. CAMERON and D. STEPHENSON. 1985. 172 pp.

> *The South of Scotland* (third edition). D. C. GREIG. 1971. 125 pp.

MEMOIRS OF THE GEOLOGICAL SURVEY. British Geological Survey. H.M.S.O.

> *The Geology of the Neighbourhood of Edinburgh*—Sheet 32 (second edition). B. N. PEACH, C. T. CLOUGH, L. W. HINXMAN, J. S. GRANT WILSON, C. B. CRAMPTON, H. B. MAUFE and E. B. BAILEY. 1910. 455 pp. (Third edition) G. H. MITCHELL and W. MYKURA. 1962. 159 pp.

> *The Geology of the Midlothian Coalfield.* W. TULLOCH and H. S. WALTON. 1958. 157 pp.

> *The Geology of East Lothian*—Sheet 33 (second edition). C. T. CLOUGH *et al.* 1910. 226 pp.

> *The Geology of the Haddington district*—Sheet 33W. A. D. MCADAM and W. TULLOCH. 1985. 100 pp.

> *The Geology of the Dunbar district*—Sheet 33E. A. DAVIES, A. D. MCADAM and I. B. CAMERON. 1986. 70 pp.

Text References

ANON. 1972. *Barns Ness.* 32 pp. East Lothian County Council, North Berwick.

ASHURST, J. and DIMES F. G. 1977. *Stone in building, its use and potential today.* Architectural Press Ltd., London.

BAIRD, W. and SMELLIE J. L. 1980. On the Polton landslide of December 1979. *Edinb. Geol.* No. 8, 9–14.

BARNARD, P. D. W. and LONG, A. G. 1973. On the structure of a petrified stem and some associated seeds from the Lower Carboniferous rocks of East Lothian, Scotland. *Trans. Roy. Soc. Edinb.* **69,** 91–108.

BENNETT, J. A. E. 1945. Some Occurrences of leucite in East Lothian. *Trans. Edinb. Geol. Soc.* **14,** 34–52.

BLACK, G. P. 1966. *The Geology of Arthur's Seat.* Oliver and Boyd. Edinburgh.

BRIGGS, D. E. G. and CLARKSON, E. N. K. 1983. The Lower Carboniferous Granton Shrimp-bed, Edinburgh. *In* BRIGGS, D. E. G. and LANE, P. D. Trilobites and other early arthropods: papers in honour of Professor H. B. Whittington, F.R.S. *Spec. Pap. Paleont.* **30,** 161–178.

CADELL, H. M. 1925. *The Rocks of West Lothian.* Oliver and Boyd, Edinburgh.

CAMERON, I. B. and STEPHENSON, D. 1985. The Midland Valley of Scotland (third edition). *Brit. Reg. Geol. Brit. Geol. Surv.*

CARRUTHERS, R. G., CALDWELL, W., BAILEY, E. M. and CONACHER, H. R. J. 1927. The Oil-Shales of the Lothian (third edition). *Mem. Geol. Surv. G.B.*

CLARK, R. H. 1956. A petrological study of the Arthur's Seat Volcano. *Trans. Roy. Soc. Edinb.* **63,** 37–70.

CLARKSON, E. N. K. and HOWELLS, Y. 1981. Upper Llandovery trilobites from the Pentland Hills, near Edinburgh. *Palaeontology*, **24**, 507–536, pls 77–82.

CLOUGH, C. T., BARROW, G., CRAMPTON, C. B., MAUFE, H. B., BAILEY, E. B. and ANDERSON, E. M. 1910. The Geology of East Lothian (second edition). *Mem. Geol. Surv. G.B.*

CRAIG, G. 1892. On building stones used in Edinburgh: their geological sources, relative durability and other characteristics. *Trans. Edinb. Geol. Soc.* **6**, 254–273.

CRAIG, G. Y. (Editor). 1983. *The Geology of Scotland* (second edition). 472 pp. Scottish Academic Press. Edinburgh.

CRAIG, G. Y., MCINTYRE, D. B. and WATERSTON, C. D. 1978. *James Hutton's Theory of the Earth; the lost drawings.* 67 pp. Scottish Academic Press. Edinburgh.

DAVIES, A. and GREIG, D. C. 1971. Comptes Rendus (Day 4) 6 Cong. Int. Strat. Geol. Carb. 4.

DAY, T. C. 1916–1930. Papers in *Trans. Edinb. Geol. Soc.*
For North Berwick to Canty Bay Excursion see **11**, 300–307, 338–345; **12**, 41–52, 87–99.
For Tantallon to St Baldreds Excursion see **12**, 41–52, 213–233.
For Yellowcraig to Cheese Bay Excursion see **10**, 249–275; **11**, 185–192; **12**, 376–381.

DAY, T. C. 1929. Two large xenoliths within the phonolite of Traprain Law. *Trans. Edinb. Geol. Soc.* **12**, 252–255.

DAY, T. C. 1933. *Arthur's Seat: a Ruined Volcano.* Oliver and Boyd. Edinburgh.

FRANCIS, E. H. 1962. Volcanic neck emplacement and subsidence structures at Dunbar, south-east Scotland. *Trans. Roy. Soc. Edinb.* **65**, 41–58.

GEIKIE, A. 1897. *The Ancient Volcanoes of Great Britain*, **I**, 317–325.

GRAHAM, A. M. and UPTON, B. G. J. 1978. Gneisses in diatremes, Scottish Midland Valley: petrology and tectonic implications. *J. Geol. Soc. London.* **135**, 219–226.

GREIG, D. C. 1971. The South of Scotland (third edition). *Brit. Reg. Geol. Brit. Geol. Surv.*

HOWELLS, M. F. 1969. Cryptovents and allied structures in Carboniferous strata between Port Seton and Aberlady, East Lothian. *Scott. J. Geol.* **5**, 1–10.

HUTTON, J. 1795. *Theory of the Earth.* William Creech, Edinburgh.

JAMESON, J. 1980. Depositional environments in the Petershill Formation, Bathgate, West Lothian. Ph.D. thesis. University of Edinburgh.

JAMIESON, S. (Editor). 1984. *The Water of Leith.* 194 pp. The Water of Leith Project Group. Edinburgh.

LAMONT, A. 1947. Gala-Tarannon beds in the Pentland Hills, near Edinburgh. *Geol. Mag.* **84**, 193–208; 289–303.

LAURIE, M. 1892. On some eurypterid remains from the Upper Silurian rocks of the Pentland Hills. *Trans. Roy. Soc. Edinb.* **37**, 151–161.

LAURIE, M. 1899. On a Silurian scorpion and some additional eurypterid remains from the Pentland Hills. *Trans. Roy. Soc. Edinb.* **39**, pls 1–5.

LEYS, C. A. 1982. Volcanic and sedimentary processes in phreatomagmatic volcanoes. Ph.D. thesis, University of Leeds.

LORENZ, V. 1972. Sekundare Rotfärbung in Rotleigenden der Saar-Nahe-Senke, SW-Deutschland. *Neues Jb. Geol. Paläont.* (Mh), **6**, 356–370.

MCADAM, A. D. and TULLOCH, W. 1985. The Geology of the Haddington district. *Mem. Geol. Surv. G.B.*

MACGIBBON, D. and ROSS, T. 1887. *The castellated and domestic architecture of Scotland.* T. and A. Constable. Edinburgh.

MACGREGOR, A. G. 1928. The classification of Scottish Carboniferous olivine-basalts and mugearites. *Trans. Geol. Soc. Glasg.* **18**, 324–360.

MACGREGOR, A. G. and ENNOS, T. R. 1922. The Traprain Law phonolite. *Geol. Mag.* **59**, 514–523.

MACGREGOR, M. and HALDANE, D. 1933. The Economic Geology of the Central Coalfield, Area III, Bo'ness and Linlithgow. *Mem. Geol. Surv. G.B.*

MARTIN, N. R. 1955. Lower Carboniferous volcanism, near North Berwick, Scotland. *Bull. Geol. Surv. G.B.* **7**, 90–99.

MILNER, A. R. 1985. Scottish window on terrestrial life in the Lower Carboniferous. *Nature* **314**, 320–1.

MITCHELL, G. H. and MYKURA, W. 1962. The Geology of the Neighbourhood of Edinburgh (third edition). *Mem. Geol. Surv. G.B.*

MUIR, R. O. and WALTON, E. K. 1957. The East Kirkton limestone. *Trans. Geol. Soc. Glasg.* **22**, 157–168.

MYKURA, W. 1960. The Lower Old Red Sandstone igneous rocks of the Pentland Hills. *Bull. Geol. Surv. G.B.* **16**, 131–55.

PEACH, B. N. 1908. *In* Cochrane's Pentland Walks (first edition only), 130–150.

PEACH B. N., and HORNE, J. 1899. The Silurian rocks of Britain, Vol. 1, Scotland. *Mem. Geol. Surv. G.B.*

PEACH, B. N. *et al.* 1910. The Geology of the neighbourhood of Edinburgh (second edition). *Mem. Geol. Surv. G.B.*

PLAYFAIR, J. 1805. Biographical Account of the late Dr James Hutton. *Trans. Roy. Soc. Edinb.* **5**, 39–99.

SCOTT, A. G., GALTIER, J. and CLAYTON, G. 1985. The distribution of Lower Carboniferous anatomically preserved floras in Western Europe. *Trans. Roy. Soc. Edinb. Earth Sci.*

SHEPHERD, T. H. 1829. Modern Athens Displayed in a Series of Views. James and Co. London.

SIMPSON, J. B. 1928. Notes on the geology of the Kidlaw District, East Lothian. *Trans. Edinb. Geol. Soc.* **12**, 111–113.

SINCLAIR, J. 1794. The Statistical Account of Scotland, **10**. Edinburgh.

SMITH, S. M. 1972. Palaeoecology of post-glacial beaches in East Lothian. *Scott. J. Geol.* **8**, 31–49.

STEPHENSON, D. 1983. Polymetallic mineralisation in Carboniferous rocks at Hilderston, near Bathgate, central Scotland. *Min. Rec. Prog. Rep. Inst. Geol. Sci.* No. 68, 42 pp.

TAIT, D. 1925. The rocks between Leith and Granton, with historical notes on the working of the Wardie Coal. *Trans. Edinb. Geol. Soc.* **11**, 346–351.

TIPPER, J. C. 1976. The stratigraphy of the North Esk Inlier, Midlothian, Scotland. *Scott. J. Geol.* **12**, 15–25.

TOMKEIEFF, S. I. 1952. Analcite-trachybasalt inclusions in the phonolite of Traprain Law. *Trans. Edinb. Geol. Soc.* **15**, 360–373.

TRAQUAIR, R. H. 1877–1914. The ganoid fishes of the British Carboniferous formations. Part 1—Palaeoniscidae. *Palaeontogr. Soc. (Monograph)*, **31**, 1–186.

TRAQUAIR, R. H. 1903. On the distribution of fossil fish remains in the Carboniferous rocks of the Edinburgh District. *Trans. Roy. Soc. Edinb.* **40**, 687–707.

TULLOCH, W. and WALTON, H. S. 1958. The Geology of the Midlothian Coalfield. *Mem. Geol. Surv. G.B.*

WALKER, F. 1923. The Igneous Geology of the Dalmeny District. *Trans. Roy. Soc. Edinb.* **53**, (2), 361–375.

WALKER, G. P. L. and CROASDALE, R. 1972. Characteristics of some basaltic pyroclasts. *Bull. volcan.* **35**, 303–317.

WATERSTON, C. D. 1979. Problems of functional morphology and classification in stylonuroid eurypterids (Chelicerata, Merostomata), with observations on the Scottish Silurian Stylonuroidea. *Trans. Roy. Soc. Edinb.* **70**, 251–322, pls 1–6.

WHYTE, M. 1973. The palaeoecology of Upper Visean marine sandstones, near Dunbar, East Lothian. Ph.D. thesis, University of Edinburgh.

WHYTE, M. 1982. Life and death of the Carboniferous crinoid *Parazeacrinites konincki* (Bather). *Neues Jb. Geol. Paläont.* Mh, **H5**, 279–296.

WILSON, R. B. 1974. A study of the Dinantian marine faunas of south-east Scotland. *Bull. Geol. Surv. G.B.* **46**, 35–65.

WOOD, S. P. 1975. Recent discoveries of Carboniferous fishes in Edinburgh. *Scott. J. Geol.* **11**, 251–258.

WOOD, S. P., PANCHEN, A. L. and SMITHSON, T. R. 1985. A terrestrial fauna from the Scottish Lower Carboniferous. *Nature* **314**, 355–6.